THE SAVORY WILD MUSHROOM

Best regards
and good hunting !

The Savory

Wild Mushroom

By MARGARET McKENNY

Revised and enlarged by
DANIEL E. STUNTZ

With contributions by
VARRO E. TYLER and ANGELO M. PELLEGRINI

University of Washington Press   SEATTLE & LONDON

Photographic Credits

COLOR (a = top, b = bottom)

B. G. Banks: VIa, XXIIb

D. W. Grund: Ib, IVa, VIIa, IXb, XIb, XIIIa, XVIb, XXIVb, XXVIb, XXVIIa, XXIXb, XXXIb

H. C. Klett: XIXb, XXXb

D. L. Largent: Ia, IIa, IIIa and b, VIIb, VIIIa and b, IXa, Xa and b, XIIb, XIIIb, XIVa and b, XVa, XVIa, XVIIa, XXIb, XXIIIb, XXVa and b

M. McKenny: Va and b, XVIIb, XVIIIa, XXVIa, XXXIIa and b

Roger and Joy Spurr: IVb, XIa, XIIa, XVb, XIXa, XXa and b, XXIIa, XXVIIb, XXVIIIb, XXXIa

Benjamin Woo: IIb, VIb, XVIIIb, XXIa, XXIIIa, XXVIIIa, XXIXa, XXXa

BLACK-AND-WHITE

D. Gotelli: 131

D. W. Grund: 39, 41, 50, 130, 142, 143, 146

D. M. Hall: 134

D. L. Largent: 6, 9, 10, 12, 24, 27, 42, 43, 48, 52, 53, 57, 64, 69, 72, 73, 76, 81, 83, 96, 104, 106, 109, 112, 119, 133, 147

M. McKenny: 105

F. Sipe: 28

A. H. Smith: 40, 84, 111, 126, 152, 153

Roger and Joy Spurr: 93, 99, 125, 137

C. F. Todd: 107

F. R. Van De Bogart, Jr.: 120

Benjamin Woo: 22, 91

S. M. Zeller: 127

All black-and-white illustrations not listed above are by D. E. Stuntz.

Copyright © 1962, 1971 by the University of Washington Press
Library of Congress Catalog Card Number 78-160288
Printed in the United States of America

This book is a revised and enlarged edition of *The Savory Wild Mushroom* by Margaret McKenny, first published by the University of Washington Press in 1962.

Preface

Margaret McKenny's long and active life was marked with a genuine love of nature and all of its creatures, and an unusual ability to communicate her enthusiasm to others. Mushrooms were one of her special interests, and she introduced many a person to the fascinating hobby of mushroom study. Pleased with the success of her *Savory Wild Mushroom,* she hoped that there might someday be a new and enlarged edition of it. Those of us who have worked together in preparing this second edition would like to think of our efforts as a tribute to the memory of a very remarkable woman. We hope that the users of the new book will find in it still something of the spirit of its original author.

The region covered by this handbook is primarily that known as the Pacific Northwest, comprising northern Oregon, Washington, northern Idaho, and southern British Columbia. About 11 percent of the species included occur only in this region, or only rarely outside of it. The remaining 89 percent one could expect to find in many other areas, and thus the handbook should be useful in much of North America beyond the northwestern states.

The number of species in the new edition has been increased from 84 to 156, in keeping with the increase in interest in mushrooms evident over the last few years. In nine genera the number of species has been doubled or more than doubled, and several common mushrooms omitted from the first edition have been added. Each species is illustrated in black and white, and the number of illustrations in color has been increased by a third. Genera are arranged in groups corresponding to the general type of fruiting body (for example, boletes, gilled mushrooms, puffballs, and so forth), since the original grouping as poisonous, edible, and "nonpoisonous to be avoided" proved to be confusing to the amateur who often did not know whether the specimen he had in hand was edible or not. Within the largest group, the gilled mushrooms, subgroupings are made on the basis of spore color. The sequence of genera within subgroups is explained in the introductory paragraph under gilled mushrooms.

Dr. Varro Tyler has revised his valuable chapter on mushroom toxins, adding new data discovered since 1962. A new chapter, contributed by Dr. Angelo Pellegrini, gives in characteristically vigorous and delightful style many of the basic procedures for preparing, cooking, and preserving mushrooms. This chapter serves as an introduction to the section on mushroom recipes, which has been somewhat shortened by the omission of some of the simpler recipes that seem adequately dealt with by Dr. Pellegrini's remarks. To both Drs. Tyler and Pellegrini I should like to express my thanks for their contributions, which add much to the value of this handbook. I should also like to thank the several persons who contributed photographs; their names will be found in the list of photographic credits.

D. E. STUNTZ

May, 1971
Seattle, Washington

Contents

Illustrations

XXXII. Orange Fairy Cup   *Aleuria aurantia*
       Giant Helvella   *Gyromitra gigas*

BLACK-AND-WHITE PHOTOGRAPHS

ILLUSTRATIONS

Introduction

THIS book is for the mushroom hunter, an answer to the ever recurring question, "Is it good to eat?" Those who wish to undertake the fascinating study of mushrooms in general should consult the bibliography at the end of the book. Many a person who started out as a "pothunter" has become an enthusiastic mushroom student, making the study a rewarding, lifelong hobby.

Another question, "What is the difference between a mushroom and a toadstool?" may be answered simply. There is none. The word toadstool has long carried the connotation of poison. This association seems to have arisen many centuries ago, when toads were erroneously considered venomous and it was believed that they made a habit of sitting on mushrooms and making them poisonous. Actually, one may say an edible or a poisonous mushroom, or an edible or a poisonous toadstool. Charles McIlvaine, author of *One Thousand American Fungi,* was a scientist but pre-eminently a pothunter. He ate nearly every known fleshy mushroom and called them all "his little friends, the toadstools." He even tasted the reputedly poisonous fly amanita, with only a slight headache as a result. But don't think you should emulate him—it is truly dangerous to experiment.

Mushrooms belong to the group of plants called fungi. Because they have no chlorophyll, the green substance that enables leafy plants in the presence of sunlight to manufacture their own food, fungi must obtain their food from living plants or animals or from their remains after death.

Some of the fungi are parasitic, existing on living plants or animals. In this division are the smuts and rusts on grains and other plants, and certain destructive mushroom growths in the forest, all of which cause great losses in crops and timber. Parasitic fungi also cause diseases such as ringworm, barber's itch, athlete's foot, and several other more serious afflictions.

Most fungi, however, are saprophytic, living on decayed vegetable and animal remains in a variety of situations. Quite a few of these are beneficial; the molds, for example, which are regarded by most people only as an ever-present nuisance, give us many of the antibiotics so useful in modern medicine. The chance observation that certain of the molds that make the blue-green growths on bread or cheese could stop bacterial growth led to investigation of what was stopping the growth. Enormously stimulated by the needs of war, the search for these bacterium-combating substances was soon extended to a variety of fungi, including mushrooms. Out of this research has come a great number of "wonder drugs," effective against many bacteria, but not all equally useful. Some of the most effective (including several of those produced by mushrooms) are unfortunately also too poisonous to man to be used as medicine. The search continues, however, and new substances are being found continually.

In this book we deal with the larger of the saprophytic fungi that live on organic matter in the fields and forests. They are valuable to man because through their work and that of various bacteria all debris in time returns to soil. Many of them are also the trophies of the mushroom gatherer, the gastronomic joy of the gourmet.

Mushrooms and the rest of the fungi are reproduced by minute bodies called spores, a part of the fruiting body itself. These spores are so fine that their forms and markings can be determined only under a powerful microscope, and are produced in such vast numbers that the air is always full of them. An ordinary meadow mushroom can release nearly a million, and a giant puffball many more.

When one of these millions of spores settles on the proper habitat, it sprouts and soon grows into a mass of threads or a felty mass called mycelium (plural, mycelia). This is the true mushroom plant, the spawn of the mushroom grower. But what we are interested in are the fruiting bodies that spring from the mycelium.

Most mushrooms have the familiar umbrella top and stem. The ordinary meadow mushroom and the commercially grown mushroom are of this type. In tracing the growth of the meadow mushroom, we find that after the spores have developed into the mycelium, when the temperature is between 40 and 60 F. and there have been a number of warm rains, little knobs form on the stringy mass. These knobs grow constantly larger and press upward until at length they show in the grass. At this stage each contains a cap and a stem and is called a button mushroom.

As it grows upward the cap expands into a spread umbrella shape, forming the mature plant. On the undersurface of the cap are numerous knifelike folds or plates called gills; these gills radiate from the center to the edge of the cap, like spokes in a wheel. In the meadow mushroom and in many others, the immature gills are protected by a white membrane, the partial veil, which reaches from the stem to the margin of the cap. As the cap expands, the veil breaks, part of it hanging on the stem as an annulus or ring. Occasionally particles of this veil make a fringe on the edge of the cap. The gills, or reproductive portion of the mushroom, are now free to release their myriad spores.

Other mushrooms, like those of the Amanita group (which contains the most deadly species), are enveloped at their early stage in a wrapper called the universal veil. As these buttons push up into the air, the veil breaks, leaving half in the soil in the form of a cup, or volva, and carrying the other half on the cap, broken up into white particles called warts, or in some species as a large felty patch. Occasionally the cup shows only as fluffy rings on the stem (see accompanying diagram).

The mushrooms to be considered in this book are of two classes. In Class I are the mushrooms that bear their spores in

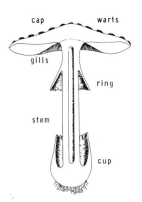

cap   warts

gills

ring

stem

cup

Diagram of
an Amanita

fours on club-shaped bodies called basidia. The scientific term
is Basidiomycetes, from the Latin *basidium,* a club, and Greek
mykes, a fungus or mushroom.

In Class II are the mushrooms that bear their spores in
minute sacs, usually eight spores in a sac. Ascomycetes is the
scientific name for these mushrooms, from *ascus,* a sac.

The greater part of the mushrooms of interest to the gatherer belongs in Class I. It comprises the gilled mushrooms, pore
mushrooms, spine or hedgehog mushrooms, corals, boletes, jelly mushrooms, and puffballs. In Class II are the morels, the
elfin-saddles, brain mushrooms, and cup fungi.

The gilled mushrooms are further divided by spore color
into groups with white, pink, brown, purple-brown, or black
spores. To see an example of spore color, take a meadow
mushroom or one purchased fresh from a store, cut it from the
stem, and lay it on a piece of paper. Within a few hours the
gills will have deposited a layer of purple-brown spores, re-
producing their exact shape.

When beginning the study of mushrooms it is wise to make
a spore print of every new kind of mushroom you gather.
When you have decided in which spore series it belongs,
check the illustrations and descriptions in the book and then
decide whether you have a find for dinner or a reject.

But before you begin to collect mushrooms for the table, go

out with an expert, if possible, for the first season. Not with a "my grandmother told me" expert, but with a scientist. He will tell you not only how to collect mushrooms for the pot, but how to collect and prepare them if you want to send doubtful specimens to a university for exact identification.

Be sure to disregard the popular belief that silver will darken when boiled with a poisonous mushroom. A newly minted dollar will still shine brightly though simmered with a destroying angel, the deadly *Amanita verna*. Disregard also the fallacy, "if it peels it is good to eat." The meadow mushroom peels easily, but so does the fly amanita, *Amanita muscaria,* and there are many edible mushrooms that cannot be peeled.

On your first mushroom hunt, take a sharp knife, a trowel, a roll of wax paper, and a few small cardboard boxes for delicate specimens. Gather only fresh specimens unaffected by larvae, and be sure to dig up all of the base of the plant. This base is often essential for identification. Wrap each specimen in wax paper, fold the paper vertically, and twist each end. Include if possible a button form, a half-grown, and a mature specimen. Then stand the package erect in the basket. If you are gathering for a scientist, the following simple notes will be of value to the identifier:

> *Color and description:* Type of cap, flesh, gills, and stem.
>
> *Where Found:*
>
> *Remarks:*
>
> Include a spore print whenever possible.

Now, taking book and basket, start out on your adventures in field and wood. Good hunting—and good eating.

THE SAVORY WILD MUSHROOM

Boletes

Boletes are among the safest of mushrooms for the beginner, as they are easily recognized and very few of them are poisonous. Those with red pores should be avoided, but the others can be tried if the usual precaution of eating only a small quantity the first time is observed. People vary in their reactions to boletes, just as to any other kind of food, and the species one person can eat with pleasure and in large quantity may prove unpalatable or even upsetting to another.

KING BOLETUS
Boletus edulis (olive-brown spores)

COLOR AND DESCRIPTION   [Color plate I]

Cap: tan or brown, kidskin smooth, rounded then flat, four to twelve inches across; flesh white, not changing color when broken.

Pores: first white, very fine, then changing to yellowish green, occasionally staining yellowish when bruised.

Stem: white or pale dingy ivory, stout, sometimes very large at the base, the upper third or quarter bearing a fine but conspicuous network of veins.

WHEN AND WHERE FOUND

Late summer (if there has been enough rain) and throughout the fall season; in spring in the Cascade Mountains, at elevations above 1,000 feet. It grows on the ground under conifers of various kinds, and sometimes is found in abundance near the Pacific shore.

REMARKS

One of the best and most easily recognized of edible mush-

1. King Boletus   *Boletus edulis*

2. Alice Eastwood's Boletus   *Boletus eastwoodiae*

rooms. It is well known abroad as the *cep,* and quantities are dried and shipped to this country. The stem, sometimes nearly as large as the cap, is edible if unaffected by larvae. Another very good edible bolete, similar in appearance to the king boletus, is *Boletus olivaceo-brunneus.* It has a dark brown cap and brown stem, and grows under Douglas fir.

ALICE EASTWOOD'S BOLETUS
Boletus eastwoodiae (brownish olive spores)

COLOR AND DESCRIPTION

Cap: light olive brown, rounded, smooth, slightly viscid when wet, suedelike when dry, four to ten inches in width; flesh whitish, becoming blue when bruised.

Pores: yellow with bright red mouths.

Stem: red, lighter at the base, stout, somewhat larger at the base, three to four inches long, covered for most of its length with a network of fine veins.

WHEN AND WHERE FOUND

Fall, on the ground in conifer forest at low altitudes in the Cascade and Olympic mountains.

REMARKS

All boletes having red pores should be avoided, and Eastwood's boletus is no exception. It is definitely poisonous, causing more or less severe gastric upset.

ORANGE-CAPPED BOLETUS
Boletus aurantiacus (dark yellow-brown spores)

COLOR AND DESCRIPTION

Cap: bright to dark rusty red or orange-red, dry but tends to be sticky when wet or in old specimens, two to six inches broad; flesh white, slowly staining grayish lilac where cut.

3. Orange-capped Boletus   *Boletus aurantiacus*

Pores: at first pale buff with an olive cast, then grayish brown.

Stem: pallid or white, covered with rough gray to black points; flesh white, changing color like the cap where cut.

During most or all of the fall mushroom season, in conifer forests. It is often found in abundance, especially in the Cascade Mountains.

In the Pacific Northwest there are several boletes closely related to *Boletus aurantiacus,* differing in the color of the cap, staining of the flesh, and in microscopical features. Probably most of these have at one time or another been collected and eaten as the orange-capped boletus, without any ill effects so far as is known. Many mushroom hunters consider *B. aurantiacus* to be nearly as savory as the king boletus and they collect it in large quantity, to be frozen and used throughout the time between mushroom seasons.

The rough-stemmed boletus, *B. scaber,* is very similar in appearance to *B. aurantiacus,* but is usually smaller and more slender, has a grayish brown cap, and grows mostly (but not always) under birch. Some people consider it inferior in taste to the orange-capped boletus.

ADMIRABLE BOLETUS
Boletus mirabilis (dark olive-brown spores)

Cap: dark maroon-brown, roughened with small, erect scales, rounded then flat, two to five inches across; flesh pallid, tinged wine-red just under the surface, firm, unchanging when bruised.

Pores: yellow, then greenish, bruising deeper yellow.

Stem: maroon, often roughened and pitted, larger at base.

Fall, in conifer forests, on the ground or on rotten logs or rotted wood lying on the ground.

REMARKS

An excellent edible species, easily identified by the dark maroon plushy cap and pitted stem and the large yellow pores. Specimens attacked by a whitish mold should be discarded.

ZELLER'S BOLETUS
Boletus zelleri (olive-brown spores)

COLOR AND DESCRIPTION

Cap: dark bay to nearly black, smooth, rounded then spreading, two to four inches across; flesh yellow, not changing color when bruised.

Pores: yellow, then greenish yellow, not changing color when bruised.

Stem: reddish, or yellow streaked with red, solid, white or yellowish at the base.

WHEN AND WHERE FOUND

Late summer and fall, on the ground in Douglas fir forests or on their margins.

REMARKS

This bolete is well known in the Puget Sound region and esteemed for its edible qualities. It is easily dried.

YELLOW-FLESHED BOLETUS
Boletus chrysenteron (olive-brown spores)

COLOR AND DESCRIPTION   [Color plate I]

Cap: dull olive brown or grayish olive, plushy or velvety,

4. Admirable Boletus   *Boletus mirabilis*

5. Zeller's Boletus   *Boletus zelleri*

6. Yellow-fleshed Boletus   *Boletus chrysenteron*

7. Lake's Boletus   *Boletus lakei*

cracking as it expands and showing pink or reddish color in the cracks, two to four inches broad; flesh yellow, may stain slightly blue where cut or bruised.

Pores: yellow when young, becoming dingy greenish or olive greenish in old specimens, staining greenish blue where bruised.

Stem: yellow below and red above, or with these colors reversed, or yellow more or less streaked with red, dry, sometimes longitudinally grooved or scored.

WHEN AND WHERE FOUND

During the entire fall season, and sometimes also in spring, in wooded areas of all kinds; also in open grassy places or even in cultivated areas, but usually near trees.

REMARKS

This is one of the commonest boletes of the Pacific Northwest, often forsaking its normal habitat in or near woods to appear in lawns, parking strips, or flower beds. It is edible, considered good by some people and rather tasteless by others; the flavor seems to be improved by drying. It is not always easy to distinguish between this bolete and Zeller's boletus, especially when the latter grows during dry weather; but for practical purposes the distinction is of little importance, as both are edible and of about the same quality.

LAKE'S BOLETUS
Boletus lakei (yellow-olive spores)

COLOR AND DESCRIPTION

Cap: yellow or reddish brown, rough and scaly, yellow flesh showing between the tufted scales, first rounded then flat, two to six inches across; flesh yellow, thick, unchanging.

Pores: yellow, coarse, brownish when bruised.

Stem: yellow, streaked brownish below a slight ring.

From early to late fall, on the ground near Douglas fir and hemlock forests, often growing in quantity under young Douglas fir trees.

Edible, but rather coarse and tasteless. The brown, rough-fibered top is quite distinctive.

BLUE-STAINING BOLETUS
Boletus caerulescens (dull cinnamon-brown spores)

COLOR AND DESCRIPTION

Cap: variable in color, but usually some shade of dull cinnamon or pale russet brown in the center and dingy yellow or buff toward the margin, smooth, viscid, often with some patches of the woolly veil adhering, three to six inches broad; flesh pale yellow.

Pores: yellow when young, becoming darker brownish yellow with age and staining brown where bruised.

Stem: with a woolly, more or less well-developed ring, above which it is yellow like the pores, below which it is sparsely to abundantly covered with matted fibrils and is dingy whitish or yellowish, often mottled with brown; flesh yellow, *staining blue* in the *base* of the stem.

WHEN AND WHERE FOUND

Throughout the fall mushroom season, in conifer forests, apparently most often associated with Douglas fir.

REMARKS

This bolete is closely related to Lake's boletus, and when the characteristic scales of the latter's cap have been matted down by rain and become tacky because wet, the two species can be confusingly similar in appearance. In such instances

8. Blue-staining Boletus *Boletus caerulescens*

9. Slippery Jack *Boletus luteus*

the blue-staining flesh in the base of the stem will identify *Boletus caerulescens*. Like its near relative, *B. caerulescens* is edible, but of rather poor quality. It is one of the commonest boletes of the Puget Sound area and the Cascade Mountains.

SLIPPERY JACK
Boletus luteus (cinnamon-brown spores)

COLOR AND DESCRIPTION [Color plate II]

Cap: yellow-brown to red-brown or sometimes with a purplish brown cast, smooth, slimy when wet, shining and appearing varnished when dry, two to four inches broad; flesh white to pale yellow, not changing color where bruised.

Pores: whitish to pale yellow at first, then dull greenish yellow, not changing color where bruised, the edges dotted with tiny viscid granules that turn dark brown with age.

Stem: with a flaring to bandlike membranous or feltlike ring whose outer surface is covered with red-brown or purplish brown slime, yellow and covered with small viscid granules above the ring, felted or matted-fibrillose and dingy white or streaked with brownish slime below the ring; flesh pale yellow or whitish, not changing color where bruised.

WHEN AND WHERE FOUND

Fall, associated with various kinds of pines; not as common as the other slippery jack (*Boletus granulatus*).

REMARKS

Edible and of good quality. The slimy surface of the cap should be removed before cooking. A similar-appearing bolete, *Boletus subolivaceus,* usually associated with western white pine, could be confused with *B. luteus*. See the remarks following its description.

SLIPPERY JACK
Boletus granulatus (dull cinnamon spores)

Cap: pale buff streaked and mottled with cinnamon brown, then brown all over, smooth, viscid, slimy when wet, two to four inches broad; flesh pale yellow, not changing color where bruised or cut.

Pores: pallid and beaded with droplets of slimy liquid when young, becoming yellow and spotted with brown, staining dingy cinnamon where bruised.

Stem: bright yellow at the top, white or pallid elsewhere, covered with pinkish tan to purplish brown viscid granules.

WHEN AND WHERE FOUND

Fall (sometimes also in spring if there is enough moisture), associated with pines. In the Puget Sound region it is especially common under lodgepole pine.

REMARKS

There are several boletes similar enough in general appearance to *Boletus granulatus* to be collected and eaten as slippery jacks, seemingly without any ill consequences. Two of these deserve special mention, being fairly common in the Pacific Northwest. *B. punctatipes,* associated with Douglas fir, differs from *B. granulatus* in its purplish brown cap and in its pores, which are arranged in conspicuously radiating lines. *B. brevipes,* associated with ponderosa and lodgepole pines, is distinguished by the lack of viscid granular dots on its stem.

OLIVE-CAPPED BOLETUS
Boletus subolivaceus (dull cinnamon spores)

COLOR AND DESCRIPTION

Cap: dull olive or dingy olive brown, slimy-viscid when wet, streaked with black radiating lines under the viscid layer,

10. Slippery Jack   *Boletus granulatus*

11. Olive-capped Boletus   *Boletus subolivaceus*

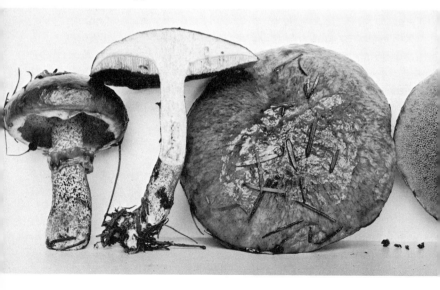

THE SAVORY WILD MUSHROOM

smooth; flesh pallid or yellowish or with a grayish olive tinge, not changing color where bruised.

Pores: pale grayish buff or grayish olive and densely beaded with viscid droplets when young, becoming dingy yellow or brownish yellow, not changing color where bruised, but the droplets often drying black.

Stem: girded by a conspicuous bandlike ring fastened to the stem by its middle, with its upper and lower edges free and covered on the outside with brown or olive slime, yellow above the ring and dingy white below, but densely covered everywhere with viscid granules that soon become black.

WHEN AND WHERE FOUND

Fall, most frequently under western white pine, but also associated with other conifers.

REMARKS

In spite of its unprepossessing appearance, this bolete is edible, but of rather poor quality. It somewhat resembles one of the slippery Jacks (*Boletus luteus*), but can be distinguished by the numerous black viscid dots on the stem below the ring and by its peculiar bandlike or collarlike ring with free upper and lower edges. The black dots on the stem are sometimes so numerous that they run together in a continuous slimy patch. The slime from them and from the surface of the cap stains one's fingers brown.

WOOLLY-CAPPED BOLETUS
Boletus tomentosus (dark olive-brown spores)

COLOR AND DESCRIPTION   [Color plate III]

Cap: entirely covered at first with small, matted-hairy or woolly, gray or brownish gray scales that become separated as the cap expands, revealing the underlying viscid, yellow to pale orange-yellow cap surface; hence the cap is grayish brown at first, then yellow to orange-yellow more or less spot-

12. Woolly-capped Boletus   *Boletus tomentosus*

ted with grayish brown as it gets older; flesh pale yellow, turning blue where cut or bruised.

Pores: dark cinnamon brown when young, becoming yellow in older caps, changing to blue where bruised.

Stem: yellow or orange-yellow, covered all over with abundant tiny, viscid, granular dots that become brownish or darker; flesh yellow, staining blue where cut or bruised.

WHEN AND WHERE FOUND

Fall, under conifers, particularly under pines; often abundant in the Cascade Mountains. It is one of the Pacific Northwest's commoner species.

REMARKS

Edible, but of a rather poor quality. Cap, stem, and scales are all rather variable in color, and in addition the scales may disappear completely, leaving the cap smooth. The scales become sticky when wet, and in wet weather the surface of the cap is almost slimy. The most reliable way of recognizing this bolete is the dark brown color of its young pores and the blue staining of the flesh and tubes: no other bolete in the Pacific Northwest has just this combination of features.

Chanterelles

Chanterelles, as differentiated from gilled mushrooms, have blunt-edged veins rather than sharp-edged, bladelike gills on the undersurface of the cap. Most of them are characterized also by their trumpet- or vase-shaped cap. *Cantharellus cibarius* is the best-known species and the one most readily recognized and collected by beginners. Only one species, *C. floccosus,* has a somewhat doubtful reputation; see the remarks following its description.

YELLOW CHANTERELLE
Cantharellus cibarius (yellowish spores)

COLOR AND DESCRIPTION   [Color plate III]

Cap: golden to dark egg yellow, smooth, first rounded, shaded with tan, then upturned, center hollow and margin ruffled, two to five inches across; flesh white, peppery, apricotlike fragrance.

Gills: yellow, shallow, blunt, with interlacing veins, running down the stem.

Stem: yellow, smooth, often larger at the base, three to five inches in length.

WHEN AND WHERE FOUND

Late summer to late fall, under Douglas firs, hemlocks, or spruces, in old or second-growth forests.

REMARKS

One of the best known and best liked among mushrooms of the west. Tender and of good quality, often growing in great abundance year after year in the same woods. It is smaller than the woolly chanterelle, and has no woolly red scales in

13. Yellow Chanterelle   *Cantharellus cibarius*

14. Woolly Chanterelle   *Cantharellus floccosus*

the center. A similar species is *Cantharellus subalbidus,* the white chanterelle, quite like the yellow chanterelle and often growing with it. It is equally good for cooking and is often heavy and of firm substance. Another similar species is the orange clitocybe, *Clitocybe aurantiaca,* formerly called *Cantharellus aurantiacus,* which has a dry brownish cap and bright orange gills with sharp edges. The gills are repeatedly forked. It grows on wood or sawdust and was formerly considered poisonous. It is now known to be harmless but of poor quality.

WOOLLY CHANTERELLE
Cantharellus floccosus (ocher spores)

COLOR AND DESCRIPTION

Cap: yellowish white with center roughened with orange-red woolly scales, center hollow, three to four inches across; flesh cream-white.

Gills: cream-white to buff, blunt with many interlacing veins, then running far down the stem.

Stem: cream-white, stout, five to ten inches in length, whole mushroom sometimes sixteen inches in height.

WHEN AND WHERE FOUND

Early to late fall, usually in old-growth Douglas fir forests.

REMARKS

This beautiful vase-shaped plant is classed as edible, but in some people causes indigestion. The red, woolly center and its size distinguish it from the safe and delicious yellow chanterelle. Recently some compounds have been found in the woolly chanterelle that might have a harmful effect on the liver. Such an effect is by no means yet clearly established, but in the meantime it would be advisable not to eat woolly chanterelles, at least not frequently or in large quantity.

PIG'S EARS
Cantharellus clavatus (pale leather-brown spores)

COLOR AND DESCRIPTION   [Color plate IV]

Cap: seal brown or tan, shaded purple, smooth, irregular on margin, hollow in the center, five or more inches across; flesh grayish.

Gills: tan or brown, running far down the stem, shaded deep purple at the base.

Stem: brown or purple, forming part of the cap, in dense clusters, five to six inches high.

WHEN AND WHERE FOUND

Late summer and fall, in old-growth Douglas fir forests, usually in the Cascade and Olympic mountains.

REMARKS

An excellent edible fungus, considered by some to be the best of the chanterelles. It makes a delicious dish when sliced and fried with meat.

FUNNEL-SHAPED CHANTERELLE
Cantharellus infundibuliformis (yellow or creamy yellow spores)

COLOR AND DESCRIPTION

Cap: brownish gray or brown or dingy tan, with arched margin when young, then funnel-shaped, with a hole in the center opening into the hollow stem, one to two inches broad; flesh yellowish, thin.

Gills: grayish yellow to yellow, blunt and veinlike, often forked and connected by cross veins.

Stem: yellow or yellowish tan, smooth, hollow, three to four inches long.

15. Pig's Ears   *Cantharellus clavatus*

16. Funnel-shaped Chanterelle   *Cantharellus infundibuliformis*

Late summer and fall, in boggy soil in conifer forests, often under the edge of rotting logs. Often abundant in the Cascade and Olympic mountains at low elevations.

REMARKS

Edible, but the flavor is not particularly pleasing to most people. A very closely related chanterelle, *Cantharellus tubae-formis,* differs principally in having a white spore print. What has been referred to in the Pacific Northwest for years as *infundibuliformis* is, according to mycologists from Europe and the eastern United States, probably not just that species but a group of species differing only slightly from one another. To the mushroom hunter and mycophagist who has collected and eaten the whole complex many times, such distinctions are of no particular importance.

Gilled Mushrooms

Gilled mushrooms form by far the largest group of fungi of interest to the mushroom hunter. It includes the most dangerous poisonous species he is apt to encounter, as well as some of the best edible ones. Anyone attempting to identify gilled mushrooms must be familiar with their structure, which is explained in the introduction, and should use the utmost caution in testing the edibility of forms he does not positively recognize.

Since the beginner should always try to get a spore print when investigating an unfamiliar mushroom, it seems logical to group the gilled mushrooms by spore color. Under those subgroups the species having a volva or ring, or both, are taken first, then those lacking ring or volva but having large fleshy fruiting bodies, and finally the small, slender, thin-fleshed mushrooms, those of least consequence from the standpoint of edibility.

I. Gilled mushrooms with the spore print white, pale pink, pale dingy lilac, or pale cream to cream color. (In some species of *Russula* and *Lactarius* the spore print is yellow or ocher.)

DESTROYING ANGEL
Amanita verna (white spores)

COLOR AND DESCRIPTION

Cap: pure white and viscid, first rounded then flat, four to twelve inches across, flesh white.

Gills: white, usually free from the stem, first concealed with a veil which, on breaking, forms a conspicuous ring on the stem.

17. Destroying Angel   *Amanita verna*

Stem: white, four to ten inches in length, base in loose cup or volva, the remains of the wrapper or universal veil.

WHEN AND WHERE FOUND

Spring (April, May, or early June), on the ground under Douglas fir.

REMARKS

This a deadly poisonous fungus, by far the most dangerous one to be found in the Puget Sound region. Until two years ago we could say that it was not known to occur there, but in 1969 specimens were found by Mr. and Mrs. Roger Spurr near Vancouver, Washington, and the same year another collection

18. Death Cup   *Amanita phalloides*

was made near Lake Kachess. Whether it occurs elsewhere in Washington is not yet known, but its mere presence points up the necessity for extreme caution in considering any large, entirely white mushroom for the table. Be *sure* that it does not have the telltale features of the destroying angel: free gills, well-developed ring, and membranous, saclike volva. Chances of recovery from poisoning by *Amanita verna* are something less than 50 percent.

DEATH CUP
Amanita phalloides (white spores)

This species differs from the destroying angel essentially only in the color of the cap, and sometimes also the stem, which is greenish yellow, grayish olive, or brownish rather than pure white. It is equally poisonous, and is said to account for the majority of fatal cases of mushroom poisoning in Europe. Several years ago *Amanita phalloides* was found growing on a lawn in Seattle, but has not been reported since from Washington. However, it does occur in southern Oregon and northern California, and might be expected eventually to find its way into the neighboring states. Mushroom hunters should therefore be on the lookout for it and make themselves familiar with its characteristic features: the smooth, greenish yellow cap, free white gills, ample white ring, and membranous, saclike volva.

FLY AMANITA
Amanita muscaria (white spores)

COLOR AND DESCRIPTION   [Color plate IV]

Cap: brilliant red or orange, orange in the center shading to yellow at the margin, or entirely yellow, first rounded then flattened and somewhat upturned, with cream-white or white

19. Fly Amanita   *Amanita muscaria*

20. Panther Amanita   *Amanita pantherina*

particles or warts covering the surface and often adhering to the margin, three to twelve inches across; flesh white.

Gills: white or cream-white, usually free from the stem, first covered with the white partial veil which, on breaking, forms a ring on the stem, portions sometimes adhering to the edge of the cap.

Stem: white, larger at the base, which shows concentric rows of fluffy white scales, the remains of the volva or wrapper.

WHEN AND WHERE FOUND

Occasionally in spring or summer, but most abundant in late autumn, in the ground in conifer forests, or on their edges, sometimes in bushes near open fields.

REMARKS

This is the mushroom so often pictured in European fairy tales. It is called "fly amanita" because it is thought a decoction made from it kills flies. It is definitely dangerous but fortunately it is quite easy to recognize; the bright red, orange, or yellow cap with its white warts is in itself a conspicuous warning for even the most unwary collector.

PANTHER AMANITA
Amanita pantherina (white spores)

COLOR AND DESCRIPTION   [Color plate V]

Cap: pale tan to dark brown, viscid, covered with white or cream-white particles called warts, first rounded then flat, four to twelve inches across; flesh white.

Gills: white, first covered with partial veil which, on breaking, forms a ring on the stem.

Stem: white, larger at the base, which arises from a cup or volva with a distinct, rolled edge. The young plant is completely covered with the universal veil.

Spring and fall, or it may occur throughout the winter in mild seasons, on the ground, under Douglas fir trees, especially abundant in the Puget Sound region.

REMARKS

The panther amanita is so named because of the panther-like spots on the cap. In the Pacific Northwest it has caused more cases of poisoning than any other mushroom. Its characteristics should be carefully memorized in order that it may be avoided. Remember: white warts on a brown or tan cap, white gills, and a distinct cup at the base of the stem—avoid mushrooms with these danger signals.

JONQUIL AMANITA
Amanita gemmata (white spores)

COLOR AND DESCRIPTION

Cap: yellow, smooth, tacky when wet, with scattered white warts, three or four inches broad; flesh white.

Gills: white or very pale ivory, free from the stem.

Stem: white, usually with a bulbous base, ring white, thin but ample, volva with a distinct upper rim that is free from the bulb.

WHEN AND WHERE FOUND

Fall, usually under Douglas fir and other conifers; sometimes abundant at lower elevations in the Puget Sound country.

REMARKS

The yellow cap distinguishes typical specimens of this Amanita from typical specimens of the panther amanita, but forms that are intermediate in color between the two can be found. Whether the jonquil amanita is poisonous is not known, but the fact that it is an Amanita should automatical-

21. Jonquil Amanita   *Amanita gemmata*

ly put it on your "poison list," especially since it can be confused with pale forms of *Amanita pantherina.*

WARTED AMANITA
Amanita aspera (white spores)

COLOR AND DESCRIPTION [Color plate V]

Cap: very dark brown, with many soft, fragile, gray or yellowish gray warts, three to five inches broad; flesh white or pale yellowish white.

Gills: white, or sometimes pale yellow, free from the stem.

Stem: yellow above the ring, grayish yellow to brownish gray below, ring ample, yellow on its upper surface, gray or yellowish gray beneath, usually with felty gray or yellow patches along the edge; base of stem with a bulb on which a few irregular zones or warts of grayish veil remnants form the volva.

WHEN AND WHERE FOUND

Fall, on the ground in conifer forests.

REMARKS

This Amanita looks like the dark brown forms of *Amanita pantherina,* but its ring and the warts on its cap are not white, as are those of the panther amanita, and it has a different type of volva. It should be regarded as poisonous and avoided.

PURPLE-BROWN AMANITA
Amanita porphyria (white spores)

COLOR AND DESCRIPTION [Color plate V]

Cap: grayish brown with a subtle purplish cast, with a few fragile gray patches of veil, three or four inches broad; flesh white.

22. Warted Amanita   *Amanita aspera*

23. Purple-Brown Amanita   *Amanita porphyria*

Gills: white, usually free, sometimes just touching the top of the stem.

Stem: with a large, conspicuous bulb at the base that is often split into broad lobes, bearing a few gray felty patches of volva that are easily obliterated, white or pale gray above the thin gray ring, decorated below the ring with gray or purplish gray patches and zones.

WHEN AND WHERE FOUND

Fall, in conifer woods at all elevations. Not rare, but it tends to occur one specimen at a time, scattered over a large area.

REMARKS

The purplish tinge that gives this Amanita its name is not always well developed. The large bulb, gray ring, and gray patches on the stem are its distinguishing marks. Whether it is poisonous is not known with certainty, but one should assume that it *is* poisonous and avoid it completely.

WOODLAND AMANITA
Amanita silvicola (white spores)

COLOR AND DESCRIPTION

Cap: white, dry, often fluffy with remains of the universal veil, first rounded then flat, three to four inches across; flesh white, soft, little odor.

Gills: white, first hidden with delicate partial veil which, on breaking, sometimes forms a slight ring on stem.

Stem: white, usually short, larger at base, showing fluffy remains of volva or wrapper, but no distinct cup.

WHEN AND WHERE FOUND

Fall, on the ground in conifer forests or on their edges.

REMARKS

Although this pure white Amanita is quite common in the

24. Woodland Amanita   *Amanita silvicola*

25. Capped Amanita   *Amanita calyptroderma*

Puget Sound region, there are no reports concerning its edibility. It is advisable not to experiment with any of the Amanita group. Another white Amanita is the solitary amanita (*A. solitaria*). This mushroom has a large base deep in the ground, the stem is much longer, and the whole plant frequently has a strong smell of chlorine.

CAPPED AMANITA
Amanita calyptroderma (white spores)

COLOR AND DESCRIPTION

Cap: yellow-orange, darker in young stages, rounded then broadly expanded, smooth, viscid, etched lines on margin, two to twelve inches in width, usually capped by a large, felty portion of the universal veil; flesh white, soft.

Gills: creamy white or yellowish, first covered with a white veil which, on breaking, forms a ring on the stem.

Stem: creamy white, rather short, rising from a large, white, felty cup, the remains of the universal veil.

WHEN AND WHERE FOUND

Fall, in mixed woods or on their margins.

REMARKS

This is an edible Amanita, but should be avoided by the collector, for fear of confusion with other poisonous Amanita species. It is a common fungus in southern Oregon and in California, and again in the vicinity of Victoria, B.C., but is rather rare in Washington.

SHEATHED AMANITA
Amanita vaginata (white spores)

COLOR AND DESCRIPTION

Cap: brown or mouse-colored, bell-shaped then flat, deep lines on edge of cap, one to four inches across; flesh white.

26. Sheathed Amanita *Amanita vaginata*

Gills: white, free from stem; no veil.

Stem: white, slender, three to four inches in length, without ring; base deep in the soil, covered with the remains of the universal veil, which completely envelops the young plant.

WHEN AND WHERE FOUND

Spring and fall, usually in conifer woods or on their margin.

27. White Lepiota *Lepiota naucina*

REMARKS

Though *Amanita vaginata* is not poisonous, it should be avoided because of the danger to beginners of confusing it with Amanitas that are poisonous. The color of the cap varies considerably, but all the color forms are well marked by the large saclike volva and the absence of a ring on the stem.

WHITE LEPIOTA
Lepiota naucina (white spores)

COLOR AND DESCRIPTION

Cap: white, occasionally tinged with gray, smooth like kidskin, first rounded then flat, three to ten inches in width; flesh white, unchanging.

Gills: white, usually becoming dull pink with age, first covered with a white veil which, on breaking, becomes a movable ring on the stem.

Stem: white, slender, larger at the base; *no cup.*

Late summer and fall, on the ground in parking strips, open meadows, lawns, occasionally in plowed fields, always in the open.

REMARKS

As this mushroom greatly resembles some forms of the poisonous Amanitas, care should be taken in gathering it. All of the stem should be picked to be sure there is no volva or cup at the base. There is a form of this Lepiota that has a gray cap, sometimes densely covered with minute, branlike gray scales, but in all other ways resembles the normal white form. This gray form is reported to cause stomach upset in some persons, whereas others eat it with no ill effects. It should, of course, be tried cautiously the first time.

BARSS'S LEPIOTA
Lepiota barssii (white spores)

COLOR AND DESCRIPTION

Cap: gray to drab with many close-pressed darker scales, dry, first rounded then flat, four to nine inches in width; flesh white, then grayish.

Gills: white, first covered with a white veil.

Stem: white, not larger at the base, having a large ring formed from the breaking of the veil.

WHEN AND WHERE FOUND

Fall, on the ground in meadows, in plowed fields, sometimes by straw piles or near manure heaps. It grows abundantly in the Willamette Valley of Oregon and may be found in the Puget Sound region.

REMARKS

A desirable edible mushroom, distinguished from the white lepiota by the conspicuous scales on its top.

28. Barss's Lepiota   *Lepiota barssii*

29. Shaggy Lepiota   *Lepiota rachodes*

SHAGGY LEPIOTA
Lepiota rachodes (white spores)

Cap: tan or fawn color in young specimens, but as cap expands the cuticle breaks into pointed scales, giving the rough and shaggy appearance, first rounded then flat, three to ten inches across; flesh white, then grayish, turning pinkish to red when broken or bruised.

Gills: white, soft, free from the stem, first covered with a thick veil.

Stem: white, much larger at the base, having a large, thick ring, the remains of the veil.

WHEN AND WHERE FOUND

Fall or occasionally late summer, in the open near outbuildings, on lawns, in meadows, along roadsides.

REMARKS

The shaggy lepiota is quite similar in appearance to the poisonous, green-gilled *Lepiota molybdites;* in fact, it would be very difficult to tell the difference between the buttons of the two species. The green-gilled lepiota, however, has not so far been reported north of southern California on the Pacific Coast, so there would seem to be little danger of being poisoned by it in northern California or the Pacific Northwest. *L. rachodes* is one of the best edible mushrooms, easily recognized by its coarsely scaly cap, large thick ring, large bulb at the base of the stem, and red staining of its flesh and gills where bruised.

JAPANESE ARMILLARIA or MATSUTAKE
Armillaria ponderosa (white spores)

COLOR AND DESCRIPTION   [Color plate VI]

Cap: white, sometimes streaked with brown, rounded then flat, to ten inches across; flesh white, firm, aromatic.

30. Japanese Armillaria or Matsutake   *Armillaria ponderosa*

31. Zeller's Armillaria   *Armillaria zelleri*

Gills: white or creamy tan, becoming brownish with age, crowded, first hidden with a white veil.

Stem: white, long, tapering to base, showing remains of thick, soft veil which usually forms a conspicuous, flaring ring.

WHEN AND WHERE FOUND

Early to late fall, in the mountains under conifers, or along the Pacific coast under pine and in thickets of black huckleberries and rhododendrons.

REMARKS

This mushroom is well known to the Japanese in the Puget Sound region. Great quantities of it are gathered every fall. By some it is considered an excellent edible species, others dislike the flavor and rather tough texture. The pungently sweet, aromatic odor is a distinguishing feature not easily forgotten once you have experienced it. A closely related species, *Armillaria caligata,* of smaller and more slender stature and bearing large dark scales on the cap and dark patches on the stem, is the only other mushroom in the Puget Sound area with exactly the same odor. It is also edible, but much less common than the Japanese armillaria.

ZELLER'S ARMILLARIA
Armillaria zelleri (white spores)

COLOR AND DESCRIPTION   [Color plate VII]

Cap: mottled orange, olive green, and brown, or sometimes merely orange or brown, smooth, slimy when wet, shining and appearing varnished when dry, four to eight inches broad; flesh white, firm, with odor and taste rather like fresh meal, but with an added pungent, somewhat metallic component.

Gills: white or pallid cream, becoming spotted and stained with orange-brown, attached to the stem, thin, close.

Stem: short and thick, tapering at the base, with a flaring, ragged ring that often collapses on the stem, white or pallid above the ring, stained and mottled with brown or orange below.

WHEN AND WHERE FOUND

Fall, in conifer forests throughout the Pacific Northwest. One of the commonest mushrooms.

REMARKS

Reported as edible, but one certainly should try it cautiously at first. Most people find the odor and taste unpleasant.

HONEY MUSHROOM
Armillaria mellea (white spores)

COLOR AND DESCRIPTION

Cap: honey-colored, varying through shades of tan to dark brown, first rounded then flat with slightly upturned margin that shows an etching of fine lines, from three to six inches in width; flesh tan or brownish.

Gills: pale cream to dull tan, often powdered with white spores, first covered with a white veil.

Stem: tan or brownish with a ring formed by remains of veil, somewhat larger at base, usually in dense clusters.

WHEN AND WHERE FOUND

Early to late fall, in the open or in the forest, at the base of or on dead trees and logs, sometimes in a wound in a live tree.

REMARKS

Very common in the woodland, of good flavor but rather tough and coarse. Use only the caps; the stems are tough and fibrous. This mushroom produces black, cordlike strands or rhizomorphs (meaning rootlike) that sometimes can be seen attached to the base of the stem. These black strands may penetrate the roots of trees or shrubs, and once inside, they can girdle the root, or even move up and girdle the trunk, killing

32. Honey Mushroom   *Armillaria mellea*

33. Man-on-Horseback   *Tricholoma flavovirens (equestre)*

the invaded plant. This activity has gained the fungus another popular name, "shoestring root rot," because the rhizomorphs look like black shoelaces.

Few mushrooms are as variable in size, color, surface of the cap, or color and texture of the ring as is *Armillaria mellea*. A description of all these variations would fill two or three pages. It is easy to see, then, why it takes a long time to recognize the honey mushroom in all its various forms.

MAN-ON-HORSEBACK
Tricholoma flavovirens (equestre) (white spores)

COLOR AND DESCRIPTION

Cap: canary yellow, occasionally masked with reddish brown, viscid, first rounded then edge slightly upturned, three to four inches in width; flesh white, smelling slightly of new meal.

Gills: yellow, not staining when bruised.

Stem: yellow, rather short, often curved and slightly larger at the base, three to four inches in length.

WHEN AND WHERE FOUND

Fall to frost, in mossy or sandy ground, usually under pines. Sometimes this mushroom has to be dug out of the moss.

REMARKS

Of good flavor and tender texture, it is one of the Pacific Northwest's best edible mushrooms, easily recognized by its color and viscid cap. The similarly colored sulphur tricholoma is not viscid and has a very unpleasant odor.

SULPHUR TRICHOLOMA
Tricholoma sulphureum (white spores)

COLOR AND DESCRIPTION

Cap: uniformly yellow or tinged somewhat with brown or

34. Sulphur Tricholoma   *Tricholoma sulphureum*

35. Soapy Tricholoma   *Tricholoma saponaceum*

grayish brown at the center, smooth, dry; flesh yellow, with strong, repulsive odor like coal-tar gas.

Gills: yellow, broad, rather thick and well spaced.

Stem: yellow, smooth, dry, rather tall for the width of the cap.

WHEN AND WHERE FOUND

Fall, on the ground in conifer woods, often abundant.

REMARKS

Inedible; the very unpleasant odor would deter anyone from trying it. Another Tricholoma with the same revolting odor, *T. inamoenum,* differs from the sulphur tricholoma only in being white or pallid ivory instead of yellow.

SOAPY TRICHOLOMA
Tricholoma saponaceum (white spores)

COLOR AND DESCRIPTION

Cap: usually dingy greenish gray in the center, shading to pallid on the margin, but quite variable in color, smooth, two to four or five inches broad; flesh white, with a faint odor said to be like soap.

Gills: white or pallid, sometimes tinged with a dingy greenish color, deeply notched at the stem, broad, usually rather thick and well spaced.

Stem: white, or more or less flushed with the color of the cap, stout, bluntly tapered at the base, smooth; flesh white in upper part, *pale pink in the base.*

WHEN AND WHERE FOUND

Throughout the fall season, sometimes also in spring; on the ground in conifer woods or mixed woods of conifers and hardwoods.

THE SAVORY WILD MUSHROOM

36. Red-Brown Tricholoma   *Tricholoma pessundatum*

REMARKS

Edible, but of mediocre quality—scarcely recommendable. This is one of the commonest mushrooms of the Puget Sound region's conifer woods, but so variable in color of cap and stem that the beginner may find it difficult to recognize in all of its color forms. The pink color of the flesh in the base of the stem is seldom absent, however, and is a convenient mark of identification for this chameleonlike mushroom.

RED-BROWN TRICHOLOMA
Tricholoma pessundatum (white spores)

COLOR AND DESCRIPTION   [Color plate VII]

Cap: dark red-brown, usually paler on the margin, smooth, slimy when wet, appearing varnished when dry, about two to four inches broad; flesh white, thick, firm, with strong odor of meal or of linseed oil.

Gills: white, tending to become spotted with red-brown, notched at the stem.

Stem: white, staining red-brown where handled, stout, about as long as the width of a cap or shorter.

WHEN AND WHERE FOUND

Fall, on the ground under conifers or hardwoods.

37. Russet Scaly Tricholoma   *Tricholoma vaccinum*

REMARKS

To be avoided; has been reported as causing gastric disturbances, and recently some compounds poisonous to laboratory animals have been detected in this mushroom. There are several Tricholomas very closely related to *Tricholoma pessundatum,* all of which should be avoided. The slimy red-brown cap distinguishes them from the similarly colored *T. vaccinum.*

RUSSET SCALY TRICHOLOMA
Tricholoma vaccinum (white spores)

COLOR AND DESCRIPTION

Cap: red-brown, covered with felty scales, margin inrolled at first and connected to the stem with a woolly veil that remains on the margin as the cap expands, about two to four inches broad; flesh white.

Gills: white or pallid, soon flecked or stained with red-brown, often more or less uniformly discolored with age.

Stem: longer than the diameter of the cap, hollow, white or

38. The Sandy   *Tricholoma populinum*

pallid at the top, elsewhere spotted and streaked with red-brown fibrils.

WHEN AND WHERE FOUND

Fall, on the ground under conifers.

REMARKS

Edible, but has not much to recommend it. The dry scaly cap and lack of a strong odor of meal or linseed oil distinguish it from *Tricholoma pessundatum* and related species. Another very similar Tricholoma with dry scaly cap is *T. imbricatum;* its cap is duller brown and less scaly that that of *T. vaccinum,* and it lacks a shaggy marginal veil.

THE SANDY
Tricholoma populinum (white spores)

COLOR AND DESCRIPTION

Cap: rather pale dingy reddish brown, smooth, viscid (but the slime layer is thin), often completely covered with sand, three to six inches broad; flesh white, thick, with odor and taste of fresh meal.

Gills: white, becoming spotted and stained reddish brown.

Stem: white or pallid, staining with the color of the cap where handled, becoming reddish brown below with age, short and stout, smooth.

WHEN AND WHERE FOUND

Fall, in sand under cottonwood trees. Much commoner in eastern Washington than in the Puget Sound country.

REMARKS

The name is a local one used by residents of eastern Washington and refers to the mushroom's habit of growing partly buried in the sand along rivers, under cottonwood trees. It is an edible species highly regarded by many persons, but one should be very careful not to confuse it with *Tricholoma pessundatum.* The two species are very similar (compare the descriptions), but have different habitats. Any red-brown, viscid Tricholoma with odor of meal or linseed oil that does not grow directly under cottonwood trees should be avoided.

STREAKED TRICHOLOMA
Tricholoma portentosum (white spores)

COLOR AND DESCRIPTION   [Color plate VIII]

Cap: nearly black in the center, sooty gray or brownish gray or often with a purplish tinge toward the margin, with fine black radiating streaks under the slimy layer, smooth, slimy when wet; flesh white, without special odor.

Gills: white often becoming tinged with yellow, sometimes with pale gray, notched at the stem.

Stem: white, stout, smooth.

WHEN AND WHERE FOUND

Fall, on the ground in conifer woods.

39. Streaked Tricholoma   *Tricholoma portentosum*

40. Tiger Tricholoma   *Tricholoma pardinum*

Edible and reported to be of good quality. The slimy cap surface should be removed before cooking.

TIGER TRICHOLOMA
Tricholoma pardinum (white spores)

COLOR AND DESCRIPTION

Cap: white with fine grayish scales, first rounded then spreading, five to ten inches across; flesh white, firm.

Gills: white, rather close, notched before touching the stem; no ring on stem.

Stem: white, stout, solid, four to five inches in length.

WHEN AND WHERE FOUND

Fall, on the ground in forests in the Cascade Mountains.

REMARKS

This is a very poisonous mushroom, causing severe, persistent gastrointestinal disturbances, often requiring hospitalization. The large size, white stem and gills, and dry cap with small, spotlike black scales on a white ground color are its distinguishing features. There are several Tricholomas with dry, scaly, gray caps that might be confused with the tiger tricholoma; they should all be avoided. Although *Tricholoma pardinum* is most frequently found in older conifer forests in the Cascade and Olympic mountains, it also occurs in second-growth stands of Douglas fir and other conifers, at sea level.

RED-TUFTED WOOD TRICHOLOMA
Tricholomopsis rutilans (white spores)

COLOR AND DESCRIPTION   [Color plate VIII]

Cap: at first entirely covered with purplish red fibrils that later separate into pointed scales, revealing the yellow ground

41. Red-tufted Wood Tricholoma   *Tricholomopsis rutilans*

color, about three or four inches broad; flesh yellow.

Gills: yellow, with a fine yellow fringe along the edges, as seen under a lens, notched at the stem.

Stem: yellow, with streaks and patches of purplish red fibrils, top paler yellow and lacking fibrils.

WHEN AND WHERE FOUND

Fall, on logs and stumps, always growing attached directly to the wood.

REMARKS

Edible, but of not very good quality. The striking colors and growth on wood make this mushroom easy to recognize.

BLACK-TUFTED WOOD TRICHOLOMA
Tricholomopsis decora (white spores)

COLOR AND DESCRIPTION

Cap: yellow, with numerous tiny black or brownish black scales all over, or only in the center, often concave in the middle, arched margin, two or three inches broad; flesh yellow.

Gills: yellow, squarely attached, sometimes running down the stem with a thin line.

Stem: yellow, with or without a few gray fibrils at the base, often somewhat eccentric, hollow, smooth.

WHEN AND WHERE FOUND

Fall, on conifer logs.

REMARKS

Easily recognized by its yellow cap, gills, and stem, the black scales on the cap, and the growth on wood. Edible.

SWEAT-PRODUCING CLITOCYBE
Clitocybe dealbata (sudorifica) (white spores)

COLOR AND DESCRIPTION [Color plate IX]

Cap: grayish white, first rounded, at length upturned with hollow center, one to two inches across; flesh grayish white, thin.

Gills: grayish white, fine, running down the stem.

Stem: grayish, short, tough, two to three inches in length.

WHEN AND WHERE FOUND

From early fall until after frost, on the ground, usually in the open, in fields with meadow mushrooms, and on lawns, where it occasionally forms rings.

REMARKS

While not deadly poisonous, this mushroom produces quite

42. Black-tufted Wood Tricholoma   *Tricholomopsis decora*

43. Sweat-producing Clitocybe   *Clitocybe dealbata (sudorifica)*

disagreeable cases of profuse sweating. The poisonous substance it contains is muscarine (see discussion of muscarine in chapter on mushroom poisons). This Clitocybe should be carefully distinguished from the true fairy ring mushroom which grows in similar places. The latter has broad cream-white gills which do not run down the stem.

ANISE-SCENTED CLITOCYBE
Clitocybe odora (pinkish buff spores)

COLOR AND DESCRIPTION

Cap: blue-green, smooth, first rounded then irregularly upturned, two to three inches in width, strongly scented with anise; flesh greenish white, thin.

Gills: bluish green, touching the stem.

Stem: bluish green, two to three inches in length.

WHEN AND WHERE FOUND

Late summer through fall, in fir needles or on edge of woods.

REMARKS

The strong odor and bluish green color make it easily recognizable. Although too aromatic to be cooked alone, it may be combined with more bland mushrooms. Another Clitocybe, *Clitocybe suaveolens,* has the same strong anise odor and grows in conifer woods, but it is white or off-white and has a white spore print.

ORANGE FUNNEL-CAP
Clitocybe inversa (white spores)

COLOR AND DESCRIPTION

Cap: pale orange-tan to orange-cinnamon to tan, smooth, concave with wavy margin when mature, three to five inches

44. Anise-scented Clitocybe *Clitocybe odora*

45. Orange Funnel-Cap *Clitocybe inversa*

broad; flesh same color but paler than the surface, rather thin, with faint but rather sharp odor.

Gills: pale buff, running down the stem, narrow, crowded, thin.

Stem: about the same color as the gills, usually as long as the width of the cap, or shorter, smooth or dulled by pale fibrils.

WHEN AND WHERE FOUND

Fall, on the ground, usually in rather open conifer woods.

REMARKS

One of the Pacific Northwest's common Clitocybes, often forming fairy rings or arcs of a circle in open places in the woods. The European mushroom books say it is edible, but it should be tried very cautiously, if at all.

SMOKY BROWN CLITOCYBE
Clitocybe avellaneialba (white spores)

COLOR AND DESCRIPTION   [Color plate IX]

Cap: dark grayish brown or dark brown tinged with olive, flat or slightly concave with rounded, often shallowly ribbed margin in mature caps, smooth, moist, three to six inches broad; flesh white or tinged with the color of the cap, without special odor.

Gills: white or pallid, sometimes cream color in age, running down the stem, narrow.

Stem: same color as the cap but usually paler, smooth, dry, with club-shaped base.

WHEN AND WHERE FOUND

Fall, on the ground in conifer woods or woods of mixed conifers and hardwoods.

46. Smoky Brown Clitocybe   *Clitocybe avellaneialba*

This handsome Clitocybe is native to the Pacific Coast, and not uncommon in western Washington and Oregon. There have been reports of people eating it, but not a large enough number of them to establish its edibility beyond doubt.

GRAYCAP
Clitocybe nebularis (white spores)

COLOR AND DESCRIPTION

Cap: rather pale brownish gray, flat or slightly convex with rounded margin when mature, dry, usually with a thin, powdery bloom, five or six inches broad; flesh white, thick, with faint but unmistakable odor of skunk cabbage.

Gills: pale cream color, thin, close.

Stem: colored like the gills, or flushed with the color of the cap, stout, smooth, sometimes swollen at the base.

WHEN AND WHERE FOUND

Fall, rarely in spring, on the ground in all kinds of woods.

47. Graycap   *Clitocybe nebularis*

48. False Chanterelle   *Clitocybe (Hygrophoropsis) aurantiaca*

Edible, but it does not agree with everyone, and is not appealing in any case, since it tastes the way it smells. It sometimes forms very large fairy rings in woods that are open enough to allow its uninterrupted growth. Until recently this Clitocybe has been known in the Puget Sound region as *Clitocybe oreades,* a species described from near Seattle in 1911 by Dr. Murrill of the New York Botanical Garden. Whether it really is the same as the European *C. nebularis,* said to have a "faint sweetish smell," remains to be settled by an expert on Clitocybes.

FALSE CHANTERELLE
Clitocybe (Hygrophoropsis) aurantiaca (white spores)

COLOR AND DESCRIPTION

Cap: sometimes brown, most often orange, occasionally pale cream color, rounded at first then flat to shallowly concave, dry, suedelike, two to four inches broad; flesh same color as cap, thin, cottony.

Gills: orange or cream or rarely nearly white, running down the stem, narrow, close, repeatedly forked.

Stem: colored like the cap, or paler, short, dry, dull (finely velvety).

WHEN AND WHERE FOUND

Fall, on the ground in conifer woods or woods of mixed conifers, and hardwoods, occasionally on rotten logs.

REMARKS

Edible, but rather indigestible and scarcely to be recommended. It was formerly thought to be poisonous. The variation in color of this mushroom is truly astonishing. The orange form is much the commonest, but dark brown forms with cream-colored gills and pale cream forms with nearly white gills are frequently found. The repeatedly forked gills

49. White False Paxillus   *Leucopaxillus albissimus*

50. Bitter False Paxillus   *Leucopaxillus amarus*

are a constant feature and are the reason why the fungus was first described as a *Cantharellus.*

WHITE FALSE PAXILLUS
Leucopaxillus albissimus (white spores)

COLOR AND DESCRIPTION

Cap: white to pale cream, convex, dry, dull, suedelike, two to four inches broad; flesh white, thick, rather tough.

Gills: white, usually running down the stem, but sometimes merely fastened to it and not running down, thin, close.

Stem: white or cream, with a mat of white mycelium binding a lump of needles or other forest litter to the base, rather short and stout.

WHEN AND WHERE FOUND

Fall, on the ground under either conifers or hardwoods.

REMARKS

Can be eaten, but is not recommended. There are two varieties, one of which, var. *albissimus,* is bitter and hence inedible; the other, var. *lentus,* has a mild taste but is rather tough and indigestible.

BITTER FALSE PAXILLUS
Leucopaxillus amarus (white spores)

COLOR AND DESCRIPTION   [Color plate X]

Cap: reddish cinnamon color to cinnamon, usually paler on the margin, convex, dry, suedelike, about three to five inches broad; flesh white, thick, with bitter taste.

Gills: white or pale cream, usually notched at the stem, occasionally running down it somewhat, thin, close.

Stem: white, short and thick, dry, dull, often with a club-like swollen base, and often with abundant mycelium binding the needles or leaves together at the base.

WHEN AND WHERE FOUND

Fall, on the ground under either conifers or hardwoods. Often very abundant.

REMARKS

Inedible because of the bitter taste which no amount of cooking will remove. This and the preceding species sometimes form large fairy rings in open places in the forest.

FRIED CHICKEN MUSHROOM
Lyophyllum (*Clitocybe*) *multiceps* (white spores)

COLOR AND DESCRIPTION

Cap: cream-white or tan, smooth, persistently rounded, sometimes irregular on the margin, three to five inches across; flesh white, firm.

Gills: white, touching or slightly running down the stem.

Stem: cream-white, curved from the pressure of the densely clustered caps, sometimes hundreds in one cluster.

WHEN AND WHERE FOUND

Late fall after heavy rains, occasionally in the spring; in heavy clay soil on margins of roads, often half-hidden in heavy grass or leaves.

REMARKS

Edible and of good flavor, as the common name indicates; considered by many to be one of the best of the Pacific Northwest's edible mushrooms. Because there are poisonous mushrooms that are similar in appearance, but with pink spores (species of *Entoloma*), you should observe the following precautions when gathering the fried chicken mushroom: (1) Be sure that your specimens are growing in clusters of four or five

51. Fried Chicken Mushroom   *Lyophyllum (Clitocybe) multiceps*

or more; discard solitary specimens, even though you think they are all right. (2) Be sure that the spore print is white. Better yet, in case of doubt, if you know someone who has a microscope, have him check the spores. The spores of an Entoloma are angular in outline, those of a Lyophyllum are smooth. The curious soapy feel of the pale brown or tan caps and the clustered habit are the distinguishing features of the fried chicken mushroom.

CONE-SHAPED WAXY CAP
Hygrophorus conicus (white spores)

COLOR AND DESCRIPTION   [Color plate X]

Cap: red, orange, or yellow, cone-shaped, occasionally spreading, viscid, edge of cap uneven, often lobed, two to four

52. Cone-shaped Waxy Cap *Hygrophorus conicus*

53. Scarlet Waxy Cap *Hygrophorus miniatus*

inches across, turning black when handled or bruised; flesh same color as the surface of the cap, thin, watery.

Gills: yellowish or olive, blackening when touched.

Stem: orange or reddish, fragile, hollow, blackening when bruised, two to four inches in length.

WHEN AND WHERE FOUND

Summer and fall, on the ground in Douglas fir forests, or in fields and brushy places.

REMARKS

This mushroom is too small to be of much interest to the gatherer. Its widespread reputation as a poisonous species is not entirely deserved, but there is no reason to tempt fate when so many good mushrooms of proven edibility are available.

SCARLET WAXY CAP
Hygrophorus miniatus (white spores)

COLOR AND DESCRIPTION   [Color plate XI]

Cap: brilliant scarlet when wet, fading through orange to yellow as it dries, convex or flat, moist when wet but not viscid, about half an inch to an inch broad; flesh red when moist, orange or yellow on losing moisture, thin, fragile, odorless.

Gills: usually yellow but may be orange or red, waxy in appearance, touching the stem, often notched.

Stem: scarlet when moist, fading like the cap to orange then yellow, smooth, almost translucent, varying in length from the width of the cap to several times its width.

WHEN AND WHERE FOUND

Fall, on the ground in woods (usually conifers).

REMARKS

This is a beautiful little mushroom, showing an astonishing

54. Subalpine Waxy Cap *Hygrophorus subalpinus*

change in color as it dries out. It is especially attractive when growing in a bed of moss, as it often does. It is edible, but much too small to be of any importance for the table.

SUBALPINE WAXY CAP
Hygrophorus subalpinus (white spores)

COLOR AND DESCRIPTION

Cap: pure white, convex or flat, smooth, viscid when wet but soon drying and becoming shining, two to four (or more) inches wide; flesh white, thick, firm, odorless.

Gills: white, often tinged with cream in older caps, running down the stem, rather narrow.

Stem: shorter than the width of the cap, very thick, with a large bulb having a flat upper edge, to which is attached a flaring, narrow, fibrous ring, white and silky above, the bulb white but with adhering soil particles.

WHEN AND WHERE FOUND

Spring and early summer, and sometimes again in the fall;

THE SAVORY WILD MUSHROOM

55. Mt. Baker Waxy Cap   *Hygrophorus bakerensis*

on the ground under conifers, usually at high elevations in the Cascade Mountains, often not far from melting snow.

REMARKS

This massive, handsome, pure white mushroom is easily recognized by its bulbous stem with a narrow, flaring ring— an unusual feature for a *Hygrophorus.* To the beginner it might appear to have a volva and thus seem to be an *Amanita,* but none of the Amanitas has gills that run down the stem. It also looks something like *Russula brevipes,* but does not have that species' chalklike flesh, and has a viscid cap. It is edible, but has very little flavor.

MT. BAKER WAXY CAP
Hygrophorus bakerensis (white spores)

COLOR AND DESCRIPTION

Cap: yellow-brown or rusty brown in the center, shading to almost white on the margin, convex or flat, slimy when wet, three to six inches broad; flesh white, thick, with strong odor of almond flavoring.

Gills: white, sometimes becoming pale cream color, running down the stem, rather thick and waxy in appearance.

Stem: white, with a few white dots at the top, stout, dry.

WHEN AND WHERE FOUND

Throughout the fall season, in conifer woods.

REMARKS

In any normal mushroom season this is one of the commonest large mushrooms of the Pacific Northwest's conifer forests. It is easily recognized by the slimy, rusty brown cap with pale margin and the strong almond odor. It is edible, but opinions on its desirability differ widely. The other Hygrophorus with an almond odor, *H. agathosmus,* has a gray or brownish gray cap.

ALMOND WAXY CAP
Hygrophorus agathosmus (white spores)

COLOR AND DESCRIPTION

Cap: gray or brownish gray, flat or slightly convex when mature, slimy when wet, two to three inches broad, flesh white, thick, soft, with strong, agreeable odor of almond flavoring.

Gills: white, touching the stem, sometimes running slightly down it, thick, not close.

Stem: white, with a few granular dots at the top, stout, dry, about as long as the width of the cap.

WHEN AND WHERE FOUND

Fall, on the ground in rather dense conifer woods.

REMARKS

Easily recognized by the gray slimy cap and strong almond

56. Almond Waxy Cap   *Hygrophorus agathosmus*

57. Sooty-Brown Waxy Cap   *Hygrophorus camarophyllus*

odor. Edible, but rather tasteless; the odor disappears in cooking.

SOOTY BROWN WAXY CAP
Hygrophorus camarophyllus (white spores)

COLOR AND DESCRIPTION   [Color plate XI]

Cap: dark sooty brown or dark brown with slight olive tinge, convex becoming flat, slightly viscid when wet, but soon becoming dry, about two to four inches broad; flesh white, thick, fragile, without special odor.

Gills: white or pale cream color, often tinged with gray in age, running down the stem, thick, distant, conspicuously interconnected with veins.

Stem: flushed with the gray-brown color of the cap, but paler, sometimes streaked or spotted with gray-brown fibrils, stout, dry, a little longer than the width of the cap.

WHEN AND WHERE FOUND

Fall, on the ground under conifers. Sometimes very abundant.

REMARKS

Edible but rather tasteless, like many species of *Hygrophorus*. A very attractive related species, *H. calophyllus,* has the same color of cap and stem, but has shell-pink or pale salmon-pink gills.

MEADOW WAXY CAP
Hygrophorus pratensis (white spores)

COLOR AND DESCRIPTION

Cap: orange-cinnamon or pale orange or orange-buff, fading considerably on drying, convex or sometimes with a broad umbo, smooth, moist but not viscid when wet, drying

58. Meadow Waxy Cap   *Hygrophorus pratensis*

dull and appearing somewhat scurfy, one to three inches broad; flesh tinged with the color of the cap, thick, odorless.

Gills: same color as the cap or paler, running down the stem, thick, distant.

Stem: colored like the cap or paler, stout, smooth, dry.

WHEN AND WHERE FOUND

Fall, occasionally in spring if it rains enough; usually in open grassy places, but also in the woods.

REMARKS

Edible, regarded as having somewhat more flavor' than most *Hygrophorus* species. In some seasons it is abundant, in others it may be hard to find. The dry cap and orange or orange-buff color of all parts distinguish it.

SLIMY WAXY CAP
Hygrophorus gliocyclus (white spores)

COLOR AND DESCRIPTION

Cap: white or pale cream, often more yellowish in the cen-

59. Slimy Waxy Cap   *Hygrophorus gliocyclus*

ter, convex then flat or shallowly concave, smooth, slimy-viscid, two to six inches (or more) broad; flesh white, thick, firm, odorless.

Gills: white, running down the stem or only fastened to it and not running down, thick, distant, waxy-looking.

Stem: short and thick, tapered at the base, sheathed below by the slimy universal veil, which forms a glutinous ring at its upper end, satiny and white above the ring, dingy white or dingy cream color below.

WHEN AND WHERE FOUND

Fall and sometimes spring, on the ground under ponderosa pine at low elevations on the eastern slope of the Cascade Mountains.

REMARKS

An edible species, apparently relished by some people, but a very disagreeable fungus to collect and handle because of the thick slimy veil. The slime must, of course, be removed before cooking. It is not uncommon in the locality mentioned above, but seems to be rare west of the Cascade summit.

60. Oyster Mushroom   *Pleurotus ostreatus*

OYSTER MUSHROOM
Pleurotus ostreatus (dull lilac spores)

COLOR AND DESCRIPTION

Cap: oyster gray or white, attached at the side, without, or nearly without, stem, two to five inches across; flesh white, thin.

Gills: white or grayish, sometimes running together at point of attachment.

Stem: usually absent, the caps growing one above the other in series along a tree or log.

WHEN AND WHERE FOUND

Spring, late summer, and early fall, on stumps or logs of alder, willow, maple, or cottonwood.

REMARKS

The various types of oyster mushroom, whether white or gray, are all edible and, when young, are very good. Several crops may be gathered in one season from the same tree or log. If the log is carried home to the yard and kept moist, the mushrooms will continue to fruit.

ANGEL'S WINGS

Pleurotus porrigens (white spores)

COLOR AND DESCRIPTION

Cap: pure white at first, becoming pale cream with age, fan-shaped or spatula-shaped or like a clamshell, smooth; flesh white, thin, firm, without special odor.

Gills: white or pallid cream, thin, close, narrow.

Stem: lacking, the cap being attached to the wood by its margin.

WHEN AND WHERE FOUND

Throughout the fall season (rarely in spring), always on conifer logs or stumps.

REMARKS

Edible, and, according to some, of better quality than the oyster mushroom. Although thin-fleshed and rather small, it often grows in such quantities that there is no difficulty getting enough for the table.

LATE OYSTER MUSHROOM

Pleurotus (Panellus) serotinus (white spores)

COLOR AND DESCRIPTION   [Color plate XV]

Cap: dull green or bluish gray or dull brown, or mottled with two or all three of these colors, shell-shaped or fan-shaped, smooth, viscid, about two to five inches broad, flesh white, thick, with a gelatinous layer near the surface, odorless.

Gills: yellow, attached to the stem or "false stem" (see below), close, thin.

Stem: rarely well developed: usually there is a thickened cushionlike structure called a "false stem," on the margin of the cap where it is attached to the wood; it is hairy or velvety, yellow, sometimes flecked with brown or dull green.

61. Angel's Wings   *Pleurotus porrigens*

62. Late Oyster Mushroom   *Pleurotus (Panellus) serotinus*

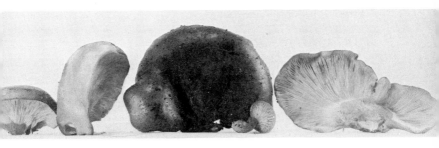

63. Short-stemmed Russula   *Russula brevipes*

Late fall, sometimes continuing well on into winter, growing by preference on logs or stumps of wild cherry, but also on other hardwoods.

REMARKS

Edible, but not of good quality; it may develop a bitter taste when cooked. It is easily recognized by its yellow gills and sticky greenish or bluish gray cap. Its preference for cold temperatures causes it to appear toward the end of the mushroom season and to continue fruiting after most other mushrooms have disappeared.

SHORT-STEMMED RUSSULA
Russula brevipes (white to very pale cream spores)

COLOR AND DESCRIPTION

Cap: white at first, becoming dingy buff to dingy brown in older specimens, deeply depressed in the center, with rounded margin, dry, dull, four to fourteen inches broad; flesh white, thick, firm, with very little odor and a mild to faintly peppery taste.

64. Cascade Russula *Russula cascadensis*

Gills: white at first, pale cream in age, with tendency to stain brown, running down the stem, thin, narrow, close.

Stem: white, sometimes staining brown, dry, dull, short and thick, about two to six inches long.

WHEN AND WHERE FOUND

Fall, occasionally in spring or summer if there is enough moisture; on the ground in conifer woods.

REMARKS

Edible, but rather tasteless; it is perhaps best cooked with meat or in sauces, whose flavor it then assumes. There has been much confusion about this Russula in the Pacific Northwest. For years it, its varieties, and *Russula cascadensis* have been gathered and eaten as *R. delica* by mushroom hunters of the region. However, according to the North American expert on Russulas, Dr. R. L. Shaffer, the *R. delica* of Europe has thick, distant gills, and spores that are differently ornamented than those of the Pacific Northwest species. The variety *acrior* of *R. brevipes* has a slightly to strongly peppery taste, gills tinged with bluish green, and occasionally a narrow blue-green band on the stem where the gills touch it. It also is edible, the peppery taste disappearing in cooking.

CASCADE RUSSULA

Russula cascadensis (pale creamy yellow spores)

COLOR AND DESCRIPTION

Cap: white, pale dull brownish where bruised or where touching debris, depressed in the center, with broadly rounded margins, dry, dull; flesh white, thick, firm, taste slowly becoming intensely peppery.

Gills: white, touching the stem or running down it slightly, close, narrow.

Stem: white, short and stout, dull.

WHEN AND WHERE FOUND

Fall, on the ground in conifer woods.

REMARKS

Edible; the peppery taste disappears with thorough cooking. Mushroom hunters of the Pacific Northwest, being little inclined to taste their finds, have not distinguished between this Russula and *Russula brevipes* or its variety *acrior* (see the remarks under *R. brevipes*). The combination of intensely peppery taste and lack of greenish tint in the gills makes *R. cascadensis* easy to recognize.

WOODLAND RUSSULA

Russula xerampelina (yellow spores)

COLOR AND DESCRIPTION   [Color plate XII]

Cap: various shades of purple, usually very dark purple more or less flushed with brown, first rounded, then margin upturned and center hollow, viscid when wet, four to twelve inches across; flesh white or creamy, staining yellowish, then brown, thick, smelling of shrimp when old, upon drying, or while being cooked.

Gills: cream-white, broad, brittle, touching stem, bruising yellowish, then brown.

65. Woodland Russula   *Russula xerampelina*

Stem: white, usually shaded with rose-pink, staining yellowish when bruised, then brown, short, stout, three to five inches in length.

WHEN AND WHERE FOUND

Late summer to late fall, on the ground in old or second-growth Douglas fir forests, occasionally under alders.

REMARKS

Edible, and considered by many to be the best flavored of the Pacific Northwest's Russulas. When young it is as sweet and nutty as a fresh hazelnut. Few mushrooms vary as much in color of the cap as does this Russula, but in all its chameleonlike disguises it has two constant features that allow it to be easily recognized: the brown staining of all parts where handled or bruised and the unmistakable odor of old shrimp

66. Pleasing Russula   *Russula placita*

or crab. This odor is very strong while the mushroom is being cooked, but is dissipated by the time the cooking is finished and is absent from the flavor. Of the various color forms of *Russula xerampelina,* the two most striking are the red form, with bright scarlet cap and rose-colored stem, and variety *elaeodes,* with dark brown and olive-green cap and stem usually white or only slightly flushed with pink.

PLEASING RUSSULA
Russula placita (yellow spores)

COLOR AND DESCRIPTION

Cap: dark violet or purple in the center, paler purple or reddish purple on the margin, flat or shallowly concave in the center, viscid when wet, drying dull, radially grooved on the margin; flesh white, thin, soft, odorless, taste mild.

Gills: white at first, then pale yellow to yellowish cream color, touching the stem, rather broad with rounded edges.

Stem: white, dry, soft and spongy inside, about as long as the width of the cap.

WHEN AND WHERE FOUND

Fall, on the ground usually under Douglas fir, but also other conifers, sometimes on lawns or in other open places.

67. Emetic Russula *Russula emetica*

REMARKS

Edible, but soft-textured and rather tasteless. Quite a few would be needed to make an adequate dish. This is one of the commonest purple Russulas in the Puget Sound region, easily recognized by the purple cap, yellow gills, white stem, and mild taste. It never stains brown where handled, as does the woodland russula, nor does it smell of shrimp.

EMETIC RUSSULA
Russula emetica (white spores)

COLOR AND DESCRIPTION

Cap: rosy red, first rounded then flat, viscid when wet, margin furrowed, two to four inches across; flesh white, firm, quickly and intensely peppery.

Gills: white, thin, brittle.

Stem: white, two to three inches in length, very fragile.

WHEN AND WHERE FOUND

Late summer and fall, in Douglas fir forests, in moss or on needles.

Considered poisonous by most authorities, but others say it is edible after thorough cooking. There seems to be little point in tempting fate by eating it, when so many safe, genuinely good edible mushrooms are available. Its distinguishing features are the bright red cap, pure white gills and stem, and intensely peppery taste (see the remarks under *Russula rosacea*). There are several closely related Russulas with white stem and gills and peppery taste, but their caps are various shades of coppery pink, rosy salmon, and yellow.

ROSE-RED RUSSULA
Russula rosacea (yellow spores)

COLOR AND DESCRIPTION   [Color plate XII]

Cap: dries to a shining, bright red, flat or a little concave at the center, viscid when wet, two to four inches broad; flesh white, thick, firm, odorless, quickly very peppery, not changing color where bruised.

Gills: cream color to rather pale yellow, touching the stem or running down it slightly.

Stem: rose-colored or red, stout, about as long as the width of the cap.

WHEN AND WHERE FOUND

Fall, in conifer woods or in open grassy places near conifers.

REMARKS

Edibility unknown; best avoided because of the intensely peppery taste. This Russula is often mistaken for *Russula emetica* because of its red cap and peppery taste; but *rosacea* has a rose or red stem and yellow gills, whereas both the stem and gills of *emetica* are pure white. In color and general appearance it is almost exactly like the scarlet variety of *R. xerampelina,* but that species has a mild taste, stains brown where

68. Rose-Red Russula   *Russula rosacea*

bruised, and smells of shrimp. Finally, there is a third red Russula, *R. americana,* first described from the Olympic Mountains, that can be distinguished from *R. rosacea* only by examining its spores.

FETID or STINKING RUSSULA
Russula foetens (white spores)

COLOR AND DESCRIPTION

Cap: tan to yellow-brown, rounded then flat, viscid, deeply

69. Fetid or Stinking Russula *Russula foetens*

70. Comb Russula *Russula pectinata*

etched lines on the margin of the cap, three to five inches in width; flesh yellowish, thin, with peppery, disagreeable taste, smelling first of bitter almonds, later like stale milk.

Gills: pale cream-white, often spotted with drops of moisture.

Stem: pale tan, stout, three to five inches in length.

WHEN AND WHERE FOUND

Fall, on the ground in forests of both conifers and hardwoods.

REMARKS

Although this mushroom is not poisonous, the disagreeable smell should be enough to discourage the collector.

COMB RUSSULA
Russula pectinata (pale cream spores)

COLOR AND DESCRIPTION

Cap: dark brown in the center, paler brown on the margin, flat or shallowly concave in the center, margin conspicuously furrowed, viscid when wet, about three inches broad; flesh white, firm, not changing color where bruised, with peppery taste, slight but unpleasant odor.

Gills: white at first, then pallid cream color, touching the stem, sometimes running down it slightly.

Stem: white, sometimes with brown stains, which are not from bruising, often with a little spot or two of orange-red at the very base, short, stout, dry, dull or shining.

WHEN AND WHERE FOUND

Fall, in conifer woods, also rather frequently on lawns or open grassy places, under or near conifers.

71. Blackening Russula   *Russula nigricans*

REMARKS

Although this Russula is colored somewhat like *Russula foetens,* it lacks the strong, fetid odor. It is edible, but has little to recommend it; prolonged cooking destroys almost all the peppery taste.

BLACKENING RUSSULA
Russula nigricans (white spores)

COLOR AND DESCRIPTION

Cap: white at first, slowly turning dingy brown then black with age, convex, dry, dull, three to six or eight, sometimes ten, inches broad; flesh slowly turning red then black where bruised or cut, thick, hard, without special odor, taste mild.

Gills: pale cream when young, gradually becoming gray then black in old specimens, changing color like the flesh where bruised, touching the stem, alternating long and short ones, thick, distant, brittle.

Stem: white or dingy pallid cream, eventually becoming black like the cap with age, changing color like the flesh where bruised, short and very stout, dull.

WHEN AND WHERE FOUND

Throughout the fall season, on the ground in forests of conifers or conifers and hardwoods; common throughout the Pacific Northwest, especially in the mountains.

REMARKS

Edible when young and free of larvae. The unprepossessing appearance of older specimens that have begun to turn black usually keeps them out of the frying pan. The change to red then black of the bruised flesh is distinctive. Another Russula of the Pacific Northwest, *Russula densifolia,* has this same bruising reaction, but has close gills and a brown viscid cap that dries as though varnished. Still another species, *R. albonigra,* looks very much like *R. nigricans,* but has closer gills and turns black directly when bruised, without first turning red. Both of these other species are, like *nigricans,* edible but of poor quality.

72. Delicious Milky Cap   *Lactarius deliciosus*

DELICIOUS MILKY CAP
Lactarius deliciosus (yellowish spores)

COLOR AND DESCRIPTION   [Color plate XIII]

Cap: orange, zoned with darker orange, often staining green with age, first rounded then upturned and hollow in center, usually two to four inches in width; flesh deep yellow, taste mild, exuding orange milk when cut.

Gills: orange, regular, running down the stem, exuding orange milk when cut, often staining green.

Stem: orange, short, stout, two to four inches in length.

WHEN AND WHERE FOUND

Late summer through fall, on the ground in old second-growth Douglas fir forests or under or near Sitka spruce near the Pacific Ocean.

73. Red-Juice Milky Cap   *Lactarius sanguifluus*

Occasionally in favorable seasons a giant form of this mushroom is found, from four to fourteen inches across. It is identical in all characteristics with the usual form. The delicious milky cap has been eaten for many hundreds of years. A picture of it is to be seen in the remains of a mural in the ruins of Herculaneum.

RED-JUICE MILKY CAP
Lactarius sanguifluus (pale yellowish spores)

COLOR AND DESCRIPTION   [Color plate XIII]

Cap: reddish brown or tan, often zoned with darker color, smooth, first rounded then hollow in the center, slightly viscid, two to four inches in width; flesh brownish, with mild taste, exuding a dark red, milky fluid when broken.

Gills: reddish or dull purplish brown or tan, regular, running down the stem, exuding dark red milk when cut or broken, often becoming stained with green.

Stem: tan, short, stout, older specimens mottled with green, two to four inches in length.

Early to late fall, often abundant on the ground in fir needles in young second-growth Douglas fir forests.

Similar to the delicious milky cap, but not bright orange in color, and having red milk instead of orange. Although less well known than the delicious milky cap, it has a better flavor and more substance.

ORANGE MILKY CAP
Lactarius aurantiacus (pale ivory spores)

Cap: bright orange, rounded then flat or slightly depressed and usually with a small nipple in the center, smooth, viscid when wet, one to three inches broad; flesh orange-buff, thin, brittle, with slightly bitter or astringent taste but not peppery, where cut exuding abundant white milk that does not change color.

Gills: orange-buff, or yellow tinged with orange, touching the stem, sometimes running down it, thin, close, exuding copious white milk where cut.

Stem: orange like the cap, slender, soon hollow, moist but not viscid.

Throughout the fall season, on the ground in conifer forests or in mixed woods.

74. Orange Milky Cap   *Lactarius aurantiacus*

75. Slimy Milky Cap   *Lactarius mucidus*

Edible, but of poor quality; the bitterish taste often persists after the specimens have been cooked. The viscid orange cap, orange-buff gills, and white, mild milk distinguish it. Another Lactarius with mild white milk, *Lactarius subdulcis,* is often also abundant in the conifer woods of the Pacific Northwest, but its cap and stem are reddish mahogany color and the cap is not viscid when wet.

SLIMY MILKY CAP
Lactarius mucidus (white spores)

COLOR AND DESCRIPTION   [Color plate XIV]

Cap: slate gray or brownish gray, sometimes pale on the margin, flat or shallowly concave in the center, smooth, slimy when wet, about two inches broad; flesh white or tinged gray, thin, exuding white milk where broken, peppery taste.

Gills: white, exuding white milk where cut, turning pale gray-green where the milk dries, touching the stem or running slightly down it, thin, close.

Stem: same color as the cap, slender, soon hollow, smooth, viscid.

WHEN AND WHERE FOUND

Fall, on the ground under conifers.

REMARKS

Edibility unknown, but should be avoided, since peppery Lactarii are not safe for experimentation. This is one of the Pacific Northwest's commonest species of *Lactarius,* easily recognized by its slimy gray cap and stem, contrasting nicely with the white gills. The milk itself does not change color when exposed to air, but becomes pale gray-green where it dries in contact with the flesh or gills.

76. Pitted Milky Cap   *Lactarius scrobiculatus*

PITTED MILKY CAP
Lactarius scrobiculatus (white to very pale cream spores)

COLOR AND DESCRIPTION   [Color plate XIV]

Cap: yellow, often with concentric zones of paler and darker yellow, broadly depressed in the center, margin at first inrolled and hairy, finally flat and smooth, viscid, about three to six inches broad; flesh thick, firm, pallid, exuding white milk that quickly turns sulphur yellow in contact with the air, very peppery taste.

Gills: pale yellow, where broken exuding white milk that turns yellow, touching the stem or sometimes running slightly down it, thin, rather narrow.

Stem: paler yellow than the cap, with small, shallow, round or oval sunken spots that often are of a brighter color than the surface, short and stout, hollow, moist but not viscid.

WHEN AND WHERE FOUND

Fall, on the ground in conifer woods.

77. Woolly Milky Cap   *Lactarius torminosus*

REMARKS

To be avoided; considered by many to be poisonous. This is a common Lactarius in the Pacific Northwest, easily recognized by the yellow colors and the white, peppery milk that quickly turns yellow upon exposure to air. It often occurs abundantly in older conifer forests, especially in the mountains.

WOOLLY MILKY CAP
Lactarius torminosus (yellowish cream spores)

COLOR AND DESCRIPTION

Cap: creamy white to pale pinkish, first rounded then spreading, hollow in center, margin inrolled with downy edge, three to four inches in width; flesh white or pinkish, exuding strongly peppery white milk.

Gills: white or pinkish, close, narrow, running down the stem.

Stem: white or pinkish, short, stout, two to three inches in length.

WHEN AND WHERE FOUND

Usually most abundant in the fall, on lawns or parking strips, under white birch trees; may appear any time in spring or summer if the lawn is well watered.

REMARKS

Generally regarded as poisonous, though the peppery flavor

78. Red Milky Cap   *Lactarius rufus*

is destroyed by long enough cooking, and the mushroom is eaten in some parts of Europe. There seems little point in taking the risk of eating it, with plenty of good mushrooms available. The woolly milky cap forms a mycorhizal association with birch trees and apparently was imported with these trees from the eastern United States. It is now well established in western Washington and British Columbia.

RED MILKY CAP
Lactarius rufus (white spores)

COLOR AND DESCRIPTION   [Color plate XV]

Cap: dull red or brownish red or brick red, flat or slightly convex, often with a small, sharp nipple in the center, smooth, not viscid, two to three inches broad; flesh white tinged with pink, exuding a white milk where cut, taste slowly becoming excruciatingly peppery.

Gills: pallid at first, then becoming more and more flushed

79. Common Laccaria   *Laccaria laccata*

with the reddish color of the cap, exuding white milk where broken or cut, touching the stem, thin, close.

Stem: same color as the cap, dry, smooth, usually longer than the width of the cap.

WHEN AND WHERE FOUND

Throughout the fall, in conifer forests, often in swampy places.

REMARKS

Poisonous. A small piece of the mushroom seems to have a mild taste at first, but after about a minute of chewing the burning sensation begins, gradually becoming more and more intense and lasting a long time. Few mushrooms are as intolerably peppery as this one. In color it somewhat resembles *Lactarius subdulcis* (see remarks under *L. aurantiacus*), but that species has mild or slightly astringent milk.

COMMON LACCARIA
Laccaria laccata (white spores)

Cap: some shade of reddish tan, dry, first rounded then expanded, often hollow in the center and irregularly ruffled on the margin; flesh dull pink, thin, tough.

Gills: reddish tan to dull rose, broad, irregular, touching stem.

Stem: reddish tan, often shaded whitish or purple at the base, fibrous, scurfy, two to four inches in length, growing alone or in clusters.

WHEN AND WHERE FOUND

Late summer to late fall, occasionally in spring; in the forest, sometimes along old roads.

REMARKS

A mushroom seen often in many situations, edible but rather tough and tasteless. May be easily distinguished from similarly colored species of *Lactarius* because it has no milky juice.

PURPLE LACCARIA
Laccaria amethystina (white spores)

COLOR AND DESCRIPTION   [Color plate XVI]

Cap: violet-purple when moist, lighter when dry, rounded then expanded, center hollow, margin irregular, two to three inches across; flesh lavender, thin, dry.

Gills: purple, broad, irregular, touching stem.

Stem: purple, shaded lavender at base, tough, often curved, single or in clusters, three to four inches in length.

WHEN AND WHERE FOUND

Early to late fall, in Douglas fir forests, or on the edge of woodlands, often in bracken.

80. Purple Laccaria   *Laccaria amethystina*

REMARKS

Edible, but of poor quality. Its color makes it unmistakable and its beauty is its justification for existence. Its only rival is the violet cortinarius, which has brown spores and a cob-webby veil.

CLUSTERED COLLYBIA
Collybia acervata (white spores)

COLOR AND DESCRIPTION   [Color plate XVI]

Cap: pale to dark reddish brown, fading upon losing moisture, one-half to two inches broad; convex or flat, smooth, moist when wet but not viscid, flesh white or flushed with reddish brown, thin, without special odor or taste.

Gills: white to pale reddish brown, rounded at the stem and barely touching it, thin, close, narrow.

Stem: dark reddish brown, very long and slender, hollow, pliable, dry and shining above, but covered with white mycelium below.

WHEN AND WHERE FOUND

Throughout the fall season; grows in dense clusters of dozens of individuals, on rotting wood, or occasionally on the ground (from buried wood?).

REMARKS

Edible; discard the stems, which are tough and stringy when cooked. Easy to recognize because of the densely clustered growth.

OAK-LOVING COLLYBIA
Collybia dryophila (white spores)

COLOR AND DESCRIPTION

Cap: reddish brown, tan, yellowish brown, or yellowish honey color, smooth, moist but not viscid when wet, drying silky, two to three inches broad; flesh white, thin, with pleasant odor and mild taste.

Gills: white or pale yellow, touching the stem lightly, usually rounded before touching, thin, crowded.

Stem: about the same color as the cap or paler, smooth, polished, sometimes swollen and covered with matted white my-

81. Clustered Collybia   *Collybia acervata*

82. Oak-loving Collybia   *Collybia dryophila*

celium at the base, about as long as the width of the cap.

Most abundant in fall, but may appear in spring or summer if there is enough moisture; on the ground, under alder or maple, in conifer woods, or woods of mixed conifers and hardwoods.

REMARKS

Edible; one of the best tasting of the Pacific Northwest's wild mushrooms. Discard the stems, which are rather tough. The very similar-appearing buttery collybia *(Collybia butyracea)* has a pale buff spore print, but is otherwise hard to distinguish from *C. dryophila.* It grows in the same localities, is also edible, and is equally tasty.

VELVET-STEM FLAMMULINA
Flammulina (Collybia) velutipes (white spores)

COLOR AND DESCRIPTION   [Color plate XVII]

Cap: yellowish to mahogany brown, first rounded then slightly upturned, viscid, one to two inches across; flesh white or yellowish, pleasant odor and flavor.

Gills: yellowish, touching the stem, unequal in length.

Stem: first yellowish, then covered with velvety dark brown hairs, one to three inches in length.

WHEN AND WHERE FOUND

Fall, continuing into winter, although it has been found in every month of the year; on decaying wood in dense clusters.

REMARKS

The velvet-stem flammulina seems to be gradually spreading in the Puget Sound region. It is a pleasant-tasting tidbit when other mushrooms have disappeared. It is easily recognized because of its velvety stem.

83. Velvet-Stem Flammulina *Flammulina (Collybia) velutipes*

84. Fairy Ring Mushroom *Marasmius oreades*

FAIRY RING MUSHROOM
Marasmius oreades (white spores)

Cap: cream-white or varying to reddish tan, first rounded, then flat and irregular on margin, one to two inches across; flesh white, thin, nutty in flavor.

Gills: cream-white, broad, wide apart, long and short intermixed.

Stem: cream-white, tough, rough with black fibrils on the lower portion, two to three inches in length.

WHEN AND WHERE FOUND

Spring, summer, and fall after rains, in grass of lawns, parking strips, golf grounds, or in meadows, always in the open, often forming circles.

REMARKS

Widespread, this mushroom is considered a pest by homeowners, but it has a good flavor and is easily dried. The tough stems should be discarded. Occasionally the sweat-producing clitocybe also grows in partial circles on lawns, but it is easily recognized by the grayish gills that run down the stem.

GARLIC MARASMIUS
Marasmius scorodonius (white spores)

COLOR AND DESCRIPTION

Cap: tan or brownish, one-quarter to one-half inch across, one inch in height.

Gills: cream-white, narrow.

Stems: brown, short, tough, polished, one-half inch long.

WHEN AND WHERE FOUND

Fall, on dead fern stems or fir needles in Douglas fir forests. Usually found accidentally because of the odor.

85. Garlic Marasmius *Marasmius scorodonius*

A small mushroom, but with a distinct garlic taste and odor. A cap or two will flavor tasteless species.

II. Gilled mushrooms with the spore print shell pink to rosy pink to brownish salmon. A deep spore print of the last-named color is apt to appear more brown than pink.

SHOWY VOLVARIA
Volvariella speciosa (flesh-pink spores)

COLOR AND DESCRIPTION

Cap: pale ivory, or sometimes dull buff or tinged brownish in the center, bell-shaped then convex with a broad umbo, smooth, slippery when wet (slightly viscid), drying to a varnished appearance, three to six inches broad; flesh white, thick, soft, with strong odor and taste like that of raw potatoes.

Gills: white at first, then pink, free, broad, thin, close, soft.

Stem: white, tall, swollen at the base, dry, dull, the base sheathed by a large, membranous, white volva with ragged, lobed edge.

86. Showy Volvaria   *Volvariella speciosa*

WHEN AND WHERE FOUND

Fall, occasionally in the spring, on cultivated ground (flower beds, vegetable gardens, compost heaps).

REMARKS

Edible, but not of good quality. In older handbooks it is listed among the poisonous species. In structure this mushroom is like the ringless Amanitas (e.g., *Amanita vaginata*), but the pink spores and pink gills identify it.

DEER MUSHROOM
Pluteus cervinus (pink spores)

Cap: dark brown through shades of tan (deer-colored), smooth, first rounded, then almost flat, two to four inches across; flesh white, soft.

Gills: first white, soon pale to dark pink, soft, free from stem.

Stem: white, shaded with brown, often curved, two to four inches in length.

WHEN AND WHERE FOUND

Early to late fall, sometimes in spring and summer; on old rotting logs or sawdust in both conifer and hardwood forests.

REMARKS

The brown, smooth cap, pink gills that do not touch the stem, and habit of growing directly attached to wood or in sawdust make this an easily recognized fungus. By some it is considered a fine-flavored mushroom, by others, one of rather inferior quality. You will have to be your own judge of its merits.

WOODS BLEWITS
Lepista nuda (pink spores)

COLOR AND DESCRIPTION   [Color plate XVIII]

Cap: purple masked with brown, first rounded then with margin upturned irregularly, three to five inches across; flesh dull purple or grayish, with pleasant odor.

Gills: lavender, notched before touching stem.

Stem: lavender, stout, larger at base, three to four inches in length, sometimes clustered.

WHEN AND WHERE FOUND

Fall until after frost, in piles of leaves in deciduous woods,

87. Deer Mushroom *Pluteus cervinus*

88. Woods Blewits *Lepista nuda*

or in needles under Douglas firs, sometimes in thick grass at the edge of woods, often in compost heaps or in sawdust.

The common name, blewits (blue hat), comes from England, where it is thought the mature cap looks like a jaunty cocked blue hat. This mushroom has long been a favorite among the edible species. The flavor is delicate but very pleasant. Several names have been used for it, the commonest being *Tricholoma personatum.*

LIVID ENTOLOMA
Entoloma (Rhodophyllus) lividum (pink spores)

COLOR AND DESCRIPTION

Cap: dingy brown or brownish gray, convex then flat or with broad umbo, smooth, soapy-feeling when wet, drying silky, three to six inches broad; flesh white, thick, firm, with odor of fresh meal.

Gills: white, then pink from the spores, rounded where they touch the stem, broad, close.

Stem: white, longer than the width of the cap, thick, shining, silky.

WHEN AND WHERE FOUND

Fall, on the ground in conifer or hardwood forests, or in mixed woods.

REMARKS

Poisonous, causing severe gastric disturbances; but its effect is more dangerous than just discomfort, as it is suspected of causing liver damage. There are several large Entolomas resembling *Entoloma lividum,* some of which are edible, but distinguishing between them is a matter for a specialist in the genus, hence the caution to avoid all pink-spored mushrooms that look like a large Tricholoma. In the Pacific North-

89. Livid Entoloma   *Entoloma (Rhodophyllus) lividum*

90. Silky Entoloma   *Entoloma (Rhodophyllus) sericeum*

west the mushroom hunter's problem in connection with large, gray-brown Entolomas would be the possibility of confusing them with the fried chicken mushroom, which they resemble. Entolomas do not ordinarily grow in clusters, and they have pink gills and spores when mature (but the gills may stay white for quite a time). These features should distinguish them from the fried chicken mushroom (see the remarks under that species).

SILKY ENTOLOMA
Entoloma (Rhodophyllus) sericeum
(brownish salmon spores)

COLOR AND DESCRIPTION

Cap: dark blackish brown when wet, silvery grayish brown when dry, bell-shaped then flat, often with the margin upturned and wavy, smooth, moist but not viscid, silky when dry, two to three inches broad; flesh brown when wet, drying pale, thin, fragile, with strong odor of fresh meal or of cucumbers, especially when crushed.

Gills: brownish gray, becoming flushed with brownish pink from the spores, broad, deeply rounded before they touch the stem (may appear free).

Stem: same color as the cap, slender, often flattened, about as long as the width of the cap.

WHEN AND WHERE FOUND

Fall, and sometimes in spring, in lawns or other open grassy places.

REMARKS

Said to be edible, but it is a good policy to avoid all pink-spored mushrooms whose gills are not truly free. This Entoloma is common throughout the Pacific Northwest. Its dark brown cap and stem, strong odor of meal or cucumber, and growth in lawns are its distinguishing features.

91. Golden Pholiota   *Phaeolepiota aurea*

III. Gilled mushrooms with the spore print yellow-brown, grayish brown, olive brown, cinnamon brown, rusty brown, or bright rust color. In these brown colors there is no tinge of purple, but the difference between a "brown" print and a purple-brown one is often slight, and some experience is needed in order to recognize it.

GOLDEN PHOLIOTA
Phaeolepiota aurea (ocher spores)

COLOR AND DESCRIPTION   [Color plate XVIII]

Cap: light gold or leather brown, grainy or suedelike, covered with a powdery material that rubs off when dry, first rounded then expanded, four to fourteen inches in width; flesh whitish yellow, odor pleasantly aromatic, somewhat like bitter almonds.

Gills: yellowish brown, first covered by a sheathing veil which, on breaking, forms a ring on the stem.

Stem: brown, fibrous, showing distinct ring, below which it is covered with the same powdery material that is on the cap.

WHEN AND WHERE FOUND

Fall, on the ground in old-growth Douglas fir forests, or on their edge under alders.

REMARKS

A large, handsome mushroom not easily confused with any other. It is an edible species, but the stems should be discarded. Not too large a quantity should be eaten when trying it for the first time, as there have been reports that some persons are allergic to it.

GYPSY MUSHROOM
Rozites caperata (Pholiota caperata) (brown spores)

COLOR AND DESCRIPTION   [Color plate XIX]

Cap: warm tan, with a thin, white, hoary coating at first, wrinkled or even corrugated, seldom smooth, rounded then flat, two to five inches in width; flesh white, firm.

Gills: pale tan, often transversely banded with darker and lighter brown, irregular, just touching the stem, first covered with a white veil which, on breaking, forms a ring on the stem.

Stem: pale tan, showing remains of veil as a ring.

WHEN AND WHERE FOUND

Late summer to late fall, on the ground in Douglas fir forests, usually at lower levels in the Cascade and Olympic mountains.

REMARKS

This mushroom is well known in Europe and often sold in markets there. It is an excellent edible species which should be

92. Gypsy Mushroom *Rozites (Pholiota) caperata*

93. Bristly Pholiota *Pholiota squarrosoides*

better known. The hoary coating of the cap may not be very apparent if the cap is wet or if the specimen is old. In fruiting bodies in prime condition, however, it and the curious color-banding of the gills are distinctive features.

BRISTLY PHOLIOTA
Pholiota squarrosoides (brown spores)

COLOR AND DESCRIPTION

Cap: cream-white, covered with erect, pointed, triangular, tawny scales, under which the true surface of the cap is viscid, three to five inches in width; flesh white, often with an agreeable odor like that of cinnamon rolls.

Gills: whitish, then brownish tan, first covered with veil which, on breaking, hangs in points from the edge of the cap and forms a ragged ring on the stem.

Stem: whitish, then brownish tan, covered below the ring with tawny scales.

WHEN AND WHERE FOUND

Late fall, on fallen logs or dead trunks of both alder and maple in old Douglas fir forests.

REMARKS

Edible. Be sure to remove the bristly scales. The rough pholiota and fat pholiota are similar species, both edible.

TERRESTRIAL PHOLIOTA
Pholiota terrestris (dark cinnamon-brown spores)

COLOR AND DESCRIPTION

Cap: brown, covered with dark brown, pointed, dry scales on a viscid, paler dingy brown or brownish yellow surface, the scales also becoming viscid in wet weather, convex then flat, about one to four inches broad; flesh buff or brown, soft,

94. Terrestrial Pholiota *Pholiota terrestris*

without special odor or taste.

Gills: pallid at first, then cinnamon brown, thin, close, fastened to the stem.

Stem: dingy ivory to buff, usually becoming brown toward the base, covered with small, dark brown scales up to the bandlike, fibrillose ring, slender, dry, longer than the width of the cap.

WHEN AND WHERE FOUND

Fall, sometimes also in spring, on the ground, usually in clusters of many individuals. It seems to prefer open places such as paths or abandoned roadways or clearings in the woods, and sometimes grows in lawns or other cultivated areas.

This Pholiota grows abundantly throughout the Pacific Northwest, and is one of the first mushrooms the novice is apt to encounter. It is not always easy to recognize because of considerable variation in size, scaliness, and color; the scales, for instance, are easily rubbed or washed off, leaving a smooth cap quite different in appearance from the normal scaly condition. It is an edible mushroom, but opinions on its desirability differ. Being often available in quantity, it is worth trying; if you like it, you can certainly eat your fill.

FAT PHOLIOTA
Pholiota squarroso-adiposa (brown spores)

COLOR AND DESCRIPTION

Cap: yellowish tan, viscid, covered with small semierect scales, three to five inches in width; flesh yellow.

Gills: yellowish, first covered with a veil which, on breaking, partially adheres to the edge of the cap, forming a small ring on the stem.

Stem: yellow with a slight ring, dry, covered from ring to base with small, dry, brown scales.

WHEN AND WHERE FOUND

Fall, in dense groups and clusters on rotting logs and trees of hardwood, especially maple; sometimes in wounds in live trees. At times there are hundreds clustered on one log.

REMARKS

Edible, but of poor quality, tasting like a marshmallow without sugar. The rough pholiota and the bristly pholiota are similar species and are also edible. The fat pholiota is distinguished by its slimy cap, dry, scaly stem, and clustered growth on hardwood logs or stumps. The scales on the cap may be dry at first, but they soon become sticky or gluey.

95. Fat Pholiota   *Pholiota squarroso-adiposa*

VIOLET CORTINARIUS
Cortinarius violaceus (brown spores)

COLOR AND DESCRIPTION   [Color plate XIX]

Cap: deep purple, roughened by small dry scales, rounded then flat, two to five inches across; flesh purplish, firm.

Gills: purple, then brown with spores, small cobwebby veil on young specimens.

Stem: purple, fibrous, showing slight remains of cobwebby veil.

96. Violet Cortinarius   *Cortinarius violaceus*

97. Cinnamon Cortinarius   *Cortinarius cinnamomeus*

Fall, on the ground in fir needles in old Douglas fir forests.

Edible but becomes quite dark when cooked. There are other edible purple Cortinarii, but the violet cortinarius is known by the dry, rough cap which, when old, has an almost metallic sheen.

CINNAMON CORTINARIUS
Cortinarius cinnamomeus (brown spores)

COLOR AND DESCRIPTION

Cap: yellowish brown to yellowish cinnamon, dry, rounded then flat, two to four inches in width; flesh dark yellow.

Gills: bright yellow, later brown with spores, hidden when young by the cobwebby veil.

Stem: lighter brown than the cap below, yellowish above, with slight cobwebby ring, three to four inches in length.

WHEN AND WHERE FOUND

Early or late fall, on the ground in or on the edge of conifer forests.

REMARKS

To be avoided; actually, *Cortinarius cinnamomeus* is an edible species of mediocre quality, but it belongs to a group of Cortinarii containing at least one very dangerous poisonous species, *C. orellanus,* which has caused several fatalities in Europe. It is hard even for an expert to distinguish between many of the species of this group, and since *C. orellanus* is reported from the West Coast, it is better to place an embargo on the whole group that to take unnecessary risks. Some of the more easily recognized members of the *cinnamomeus* group that are common in the Pacific Northwest are *C. semi-sanguineus,* with yellow cap and stem and blood-red gills; *C.*

croceofolius, with yellowish cap and stem and brilliant orange young gills; *C. phoeniceus* var. *occidentalis,* with dark maroon cap, yellow stem, and blood-red gills; and *C. sanguineus,* with cap, stem, and gills all red.

PURPLE-STAINING CORTINARIUS
Cortinarius mutabilis (rusty brown spores)

COLOR AND DESCRIPTION   [Color plate XX]

Cap: violet or grayish violet, becoming more or less mottled with buff or pale brown on the center in older caps, smooth, viscid, two to three or four inches broad; flesh violet, changing to dark purple where bruised, without special odor or taste.

Gills: violet when young, becoming brown with spores, changing to dark violet or purple where bruised, rounded before they touch the stem.

Stem: same color as the cap, staining dark purple or violet where bruised, dry, silky, bearing the remains of the copious violet cortina on its upper part, a little longer than the width of the cap, thickened below into a club-shaped bulb.

WHEN AND WHERE FOUND

Fall, on the ground in conifer forests, especially in the mountains.

REMARKS

This is a common Cortinarius of the Cascade and Olympic mountains, recognizable by its violet colors, sticky cap, and especially the dark purple color assumed by the bruised flesh of all parts. Whether it is edible is not known, but it seems that most of the large, fleshy Cortinarii with viscid caps that have been tested are safe enough, though rarely of good quality. If you *must* experiment with eating Cortinarii, the large viscid ones are probably the best ones for your ventures.

98. Purple-staining Cortinarius   *Cortinarius mutabilis*

99. Common Paxillus   *Paxillus involutus*

COMMON PAXILLUS
Paxillus involutus (yellow-brown spores)

COLOR AND DESCRIPTION   [Color plate XX]

Cap: yellow-brown to dark brown, convex then flat, finally shallowly funnel-shaped, margin inrolled at first and long remaining so, finally flat, often with riblike markings, with smooth, matted-woolly surface that is sticky when wet, four to eight inches broad, occasionally larger; flesh buff to brownish yellow, thick, taste somewhat sour.

Gills: yellow then brown, staining brown where bruised, running down the stem, close, often with cross veins.

Stem: about the same color as the cap, thick, smooth, dry, usually shorter than the width of the cap.

WHEN AND WHERE FOUND

Late summer and fall, on the ground in woods or in open places. It frequently grows in lawns, usually under or near trees.

REMARKS

This is one of the few mushrooms that often can be found in quantity within the city limits. It is edible, but has not much to recommend it, requiring special preparation to disguise the sour taste and the unappetizing blackish color of cooked specimens. Some persons cannot tolerate it, especially if it is not thoroughly cooked. If eaten raw it is apt to cause serious gastric disturbances.

Another Paxillus, *Paxillus atrotomentosus,* is found in conifer woods throughout the Pacific Northwest. It grows on old stumps or logs and has a short, thick, eccentric stem that looks like dark brown velvet. It should not be eaten.

POISON PIE
Hebeloma crustuliniforme (dull brown spores)

COLOR AND DESCRIPTION

Cap: pale cream color to pale crust brown, smooth, slimy-

100. Poison Pie   *Hebeloma crustuliniforme*

viscid when wet, about two to four inches broad; flesh white, thick, with odor of radish.

Gills: white then dull brown, with white edges, notched where they touch the stem, thin, close.

Stem: white, dry, slightly granular at least at the top, as long as the width of the cap or longer, usually with a bulb at the base.

WHEN AND WHERE FOUND

Throughout the fall season, on the ground in conifer forests especially, but also in mixed stands. It often forms large fairy rings.

REMARKS

Poisonous; it causes gastric disturbances and may have other more harmful effects. It is a very common mushroom of

101. Dark-centered Hebeloma   *Hebeloma mesophaeum*

the Pacific Northwest's conifer forests, recognizable by the slimy pale cap, white stem, dull brown gills, and radish odor.

DARK-CENTERED HEBELOMA
Hebeloma mesophaeum (dull brown spores)

COLOR AND DESCRIPTION

Cap: dark brown at the center, shading to pallid on the margin, usually convex or with a low umbo, smooth, viscid, with remnants of the fibrous veil on the margin, about two inches broad, rarely more; flesh white, thin, with slight to strong odor of radish.

Gills: white then dull brown, thin, close, notched at the stem.

Stem: white at the top, becoming dark, dull brown from the base upward, slender, streaked with loose fibrils in the lower part, usually taller than the width of the cap.

WHEN AND WHERE FOUND

Fall, on the ground under all kinds of trees, but mostly in conifer woods.

REMARKS

To be avoided; it does not have as bad a reputation as the poison pie, but at the very least it is unpalatable and there seems little point in eating it. It is usually one of the commonest Hebelomas, especially in conifer woods. The brown-centered cap with marginal veil patches and the rather faint radish odor are distinctive.

TURNIP-BULB INOCYBE
Inocybe napipes (dull brown spores)

COLOR AND DESCRIPTION   [Color plate XXI]

Cap: dark brown, sometimes with a silvery superficial coating that tends to hide the color, bell-shaped then flat or slightly convex, with pronounced umbo, smooth, soapy-feeling but not viscid when wet, drying silky, one and a half to three inches broad; flesh white, thin, firm, with unpleasant odor of chestnut catkins.

Gills: white at first, then dull grayish brown, touching the stem.

Stem: pallid at the top, brown below, satiny, rigid, with a turniplike bulb at the base, usually longer than the width of the cap.

WHEN AND WHERE FOUND

Fall, also in the spring in some seasons, on the ground under conifers.

102. Turnip-Bulb Inocybe   *Inocybe napipes*

REMARKS

Very poisonous; a few fruiting bodies could contain enough muscarine to cause a severe case of poisoning requiring immediate medical attention. Fortunately, the unprepossessing appearance and unpleasant odor are apt to discourage the would-be mycophagist, and we do not have any authenticated cases of poisoning by this potentially dangerous mushroom.

BLUSHING INOCYBE
Inocybe pudica (dull brown spores)

COLOR AND DESCRIPTION

Cap: white, becoming more or less flushed with salmon

103. Blushing Inocybe   *Inocybe pudica*

pink or red with age, bell-shaped, slippery when wet but not truly viscid, one to two inches broad; flesh white, with unpleasant odor of chestnut catkins.

Gills: white, often becoming flushed with pink or red, eventually dull brown from the spores, notched at the stem.

Stem: white, staining like the gills and cap, slender, dry, silky, with or without a slight bulb at the base.

WHEN AND WHERE FOUND

Throughout the fall season, in conifer woods.

To be avoided, like all Inocybes. This very common species is easy to recognize if the red staining is pronounced, as it often is, but sometimes there is only a hint of it around the edge of the cap. Very similar species are *I. geophylla,* with sharp-pointed, pure white cap and stem that never stain red, and *I. lilacina,* with lilac cap that fades to dingy cream color with age.

AUTUMNAL GALERINA
Galerina autumnalis (rusty brown spores)

COLOR AND DESCRIPTION   [Color plate XXI]

Cap: yellow-brown when wet, fading to buff when dry, flat or shallowly convex, smooth, sticky when wet (slightly viscid), one to one and a half inches broad; flesh watery brown moist, pale buff dry, thin, without special odor, or with slight odor and taste of cucumber.

Gills: pale brown at first, then darker brown from the spores, touching the stem.

Stem: pale brown, then darker brown from the base up with age, slender, hollow, rather tough, smooth or roughened with fibrils up to the thin, narrow, white ring.

WHEN AND WHERE FOUND

Fall, growing solitary or in small clusters on wood, or seemingly on the ground but from buried wood. It occurs both in the woods and in open areas outside them.

REMARKS

Poisonous; this very dangerous mushroom contains amanitines, the deadly amanita toxins. A similar species *(Galerina venenata)* nearly caused the death of a couple in Portland, Oregon, who found them growing in a lawn. Fortunately, mushroom hunters seem little inclined to collect small, dingy

104. Autumnal Galerina *Galerina autumnalis*

105. Meadow Mushroom *Agaricus campestris*

brown mushrooms such as these for the table. The sticky, yellow-brown cap, dark brown stem with its narrow white ring, and growth on wood are the features to watch for in recognizing and avoiding this Galerina.

IV. Gilled mushrooms with spore print dark reddish chocolate, purple-brown, brownish purple, grayish purple, purplish black, or black. These colors are referred to as purple-brown or black in most mushroom handbooks. The eye needs some training to distinguish between the reddish chocolate color and some of the richer browns of the "brown-spored" group.

MEADOW MUSHROOM
Agaricus campestris (purple-brown spores)

COLOR AND DESCRIPTION   [Color plate XXII]

Cap: cream-white, silky-smooth or occasionally with small scales, first rounded then flat, three to six inches across; flesh white, firm.

Gills: pink, then purple-brown, at first covered with white veil that forms a slight ring on the stem on breaking.

Stem: white, occasionally shaded rose, short, pointed at the base, three to five inches in length.

WHEN AND WHERE FOUND

Late summer and fall; east of the Cascade Mountains often in the spring. Grows in open meadows, lawns, golf courses, parking strips; always in the open, never in the woods.

REMARKS

Holds top honors with the morel, king boletus, and yellow chanterelle as an edible mushroom. The silky white cap, thin ragged ring, bright pink young gills, and growth in open, grassy places are its distinguishing features. Contrary to popular belief, the meadow mushroom is not the commercially cultivated mushroom.

THE PRINCE
Agaricus augustus (purple-brown spores)

COLOR AND DESCRIPTION   [Color plate XXII]

Cap: cream-white or light tan, staining yellow then orange-brown with age or where handled, smooth, covered with close-pressed, small, reddish brown scales, rounded then flat, five to seventeen inches in width; flesh white, aromatic, with almond odor.

Gills: first cream-white, then dull rose, becoming purplish brown, in young stages covered with a thick white veil which, on breaking, forms a large ring on stem.

Stem: cream-white shaded with brown, larger at base, five to twelve inches long.

WHEN AND WHERE FOUND

In rainy seasons from June to October, in dry seasons beginning to fruit in August. If the place in which it appears is watered, successive crops will be produced. It often grows near

106. The Prince   *Agaricus augustus*

107. Flat-Top Mushroom   *Agaricus placomyces* (or *meleagris?*)

compost heaps or in flower beds, on lawns, in orchards, sometimes near edges of roads, usually in the open.

REMARKS

One of the most desirable of edible mushrooms, meaty and
of fine flavor. The much less desirable flat-top mushroom
(*Agaricus placomyces*) has *gray*-brown or blackish small
scales on a white or pallid ground color that does not turn
yellow with age, and does not have an almond odor.

FLAT-TOP MUSHROOM
Agaricus placomyces (or *meleagris?*) (purplish chocolate
spores)

COLOR AND DESCRIPTION   [Color plate XXIII]

Cap: silvery gray or grayish brown, darker in center,
smooth, with gray-brown flat scales, first rounded then
spreading flat, three to six inches across; flesh white, dar-

kening to pinkish with age, sometimes smelling like creosote.

Gills: pale pink, then bright pink, turning purple-brown, first hidden by a white veil which, on breaking, forms a distinct ring on the stem.

Stem: white, then dull pinkish, slightly larger at the base, three to five inches in length, often clustered.

WHEN AND WHERE FOUND

Fall, on the ground under deciduous trees and conifers.

REMARKS

The flat-top mushroom is a tempting specimen for the hunter, but it has a dubious reputation. Specimens that smell of creosote are very apt to cause illness, and even those that have a normal fungus smell are not tolerated by everyone. It is wise, therefore, to eat only a small quantity of this mushroom when trying it for the first time, and to avoid altogether the specimens that smell of creosote (phenol). The question of the real identity of the flat-top mushroom has not yet been settled. There are those who say that it is not the *Agaricus placomyces* of the eastern United States, and they prefer to call it *A. meleagris,* a European species that is certainly very similar to our fungus.

WOODLAND MUSHROOM
Agaricus sylvicola (purple-brown spores)

COLOR AND DESCRIPTION

Cap: white, smooth, silky, rounded then flat, sometimes staining yellow when bruised, three to five inches in width; flesh white, smelling of bitter almonds.

Gills: pink, turning purple-brown, first concealed by a white veil which, on breaking, forms a thick ring on the stem.

Stem: white, often abruptly bulbous at the base, three to five inches in length.

Fall, occasionally in the spring, on the ground in Douglas fir and spruce forests.

REMARKS

Widely recognized as an edible mushroom, but it should be tried with caution for the first time, as it is known to be poisonous to some persons and not to others. There are several other large white species of *Agaricus* that easily can be mistaken for the woodland mushroom. One of these, the prairie mushroom *(A. arvensis),* once common in the Puget Sound area but now seldom found, is larger, fleshier, and has larger spores than *A. sylvicola,* but is otherwise very similar. It is a good edible species. Two others, *A. albolutescens* and *A. xanthodermus,* can cause severe gastric disturbances. They can be recognized by the intense yellow stain that appears instantly wherever their flesh is bruised or even touched. The woodland mushroom also stains yellow, but much more slowly and much less intensely than these two. In addition, *A. xanthodermus* has a strong smell of creosote.

SNOWY CAP

Agaricus nivescens (dark purplish chocolate spores)

COLOR AND DESCRIPTION

Cap: white, eventually pale buff in the center when old, convex, dry, silky-smooth at the center, with a few scales at the margin, three to five inches broad; flesh white, not changing color where broken, thick, firm, with almond odor.

Gills: white in unopened buttons, then pale grayish or brownish lilac, finally chocolate brown, free from the stem, rather narrow.

Stem: white, thick, with a bulb at the base, silky-smooth in the upper part, with tiny pointed scales or warts in an area just above the bulb, about as long as the width of the cap;

108. Woodland Mushroom   *Agaricus sylvicola*

109. Snowy Cap   *Agaricus nivescens*

110. Felt-ringed Agaricus *Agaricus hondensis*

ring white, thick, flaring, with triangular felty patches on its undersurface.

WHEN AND WHERE FOUND

Fall, in grassy places near trees.

REMARKS

Edible and of good quality. This Agaricus seems to be rather common in the Puget Sound area and is probably often taken to be the woodland mushroom, which it resembles. The small, pointed scales above the bulb on the stem and the failure of cap or stem to turn yellow where bruised are its distinctive features.

THE SAVORY WILD MUSHROOM

FELT-RINGED AGARICUS
Agaricus hondensis (purplish chocolate spores)

COLOR AND DESCRIPTION

Cap: covered with thin, rather broad, flat, "ironed-down" pale fawn-colored or pale lilac-brown scales on a white or ivory ground color, convex then flat, smooth, dry, four to six inches broad, sometimes larger; flesh white, thick, without special odor, or sometimes smelling of creosote.

Gills: usually pink at first, sometimes pale grayish lilac, finally chocolate brown, free, rounded at the stem, thin, close.

Stem: white, stout, with a bulb at the base, smooth, satiny, about as long as the width of the cap; ring flaring, feltlike, with thick, even edge and no patches on the undersurface.

WHEN AND WHERE FOUND

Fall, on the ground under conifers, mostly Douglas fir and hemlock.

REMARKS

This handsome Agaricus looks as though it should be an excellent edible species, but it develops a strong creosote odor in cooking and has a most unpleasant, soapy-metallic flavor with overtones of creosote. Apparently it is poisonous to some persons, and for those not so affected the unpleasant flavor would be enough of a deterrent.

WOOLLY-STEMMED AGARICUS
Agaricus subrutilescens (purplish chocolate spores)

COLOR AND DESCRIPTION   [Color plate XXIII]

Cap: covered with rather large, brownish purple, flat scales, smooth, dry, four to six inches broad; flesh white, thick, rather soft, without special odor or taste, no color change where bruised.

111. Woolly-stemmed Agaricus   *Agaricus subrutilescens*

Gills: bright pink at first, then chocolate brown, free, rounded at the stem, thin, close.

Stem: pure white, slightly thickened toward the base, with a thin, membranous white ring, satiny above the ring, densely covered below with patches and streaks of white woolly substance, about as long as the width of the cap.

WHEN AND WHERE FOUND

Fall, under conifers or in mixed stands of hardwoods and conifers. It is uncommon north of Olympia, Washington, becomes more abundant as one goes southward, and is fairly common in Oregon and northern California.

Edible and choice. The conspicuous purple scales on the cap and the white woolly stem make it easy to recognize.

SYLVAN AGARICUS
Agaricus silvaticus (purplish chocolate spores)

COLOR AND DESCRIPTION

Cap: covered with small, russet, tawny, or red-brown, "ironed-down" scales, convex or flat, dry, smooth, two to six inches broad; flesh white, thick, firm, without special odor, slowly turning reddish brown where cut open.

Gills: whitish at first, then pale pink, finally chocolate brown, free, rounded at the stem, thin, crowded.

Stem: white, often tinged brownish pink, and flushed with dingy brown in age, smooth, satiny, usually with a bulb at the base, as tall as the width of the cap; ring white, ample, thin.

112. Sylvan Agaricus   *Agaricus silvaticus*

Fall, under conifers or hardwoods; typically in the forest.

REMARKS

Edible and considered good by many, but it does not agree with everyone and should be tried cautiously at first. For many years we have called this mushroom *Agaricus silvaticus,* but it is evidently not the true *A. silvaticus* of Europe, which European authorities agree is a species with red-staining flesh. The western *"silvaticus"* has not been officially named, but until this is done, there seems little harm in keeping the name it has long had. It resembles the flat-top mushroom closely, but has red-brown instead of gray-brown scales, lacks the smell of creosote the latter so frequently has, and has a thinner, wider ring. In the color of its scales it resembles the prince, but it does not stain yellow and does not have an almond smell.

QUESTIONABLE STROPHARIA
Stropharia ambigua (purple-brown spores)

COLOR AND DESCRIPTION   [Color plate XXIV]

Cap: clear chrome yellow, first rounded then flat, viscid when wet, margin edged with particles of white broken veil, two to five inches across; flesh whitish.

Gills: white at first, then grayish, finally purple, at first concealed by white veil which, on breaking, adheres to margin of cap, forming only slight ring on stem.

Stem: white, larger at base, lower portion covered with fluffy white scales.

WHEN AND WHERE FOUND

Fall, only occasionally in the spring, on the ground in both conifer and deciduous forests, or on their margins.

REMARKS

Although a conspicuous mushroom in the woods and easily

113. Questionable Stropharia   *Stropharia ambigua*

identified, it is not a very good edible species, being flavorless or tasting of rotting leaves. A mushroom of similar appearance is *Amanita gemmata,* but the dark gills of the Stropharia are quite different from the white gills of the Amanita.

WINE RED STROPHARIA
Stropharia rugoso-annulata (grayish violet spores)

COLOR AND DESCRIPTION

Cap: dull wine red or purplish red at first, finally fading to straw color, convex, dry, smooth, silky, three to six, sometimes eight, inches broad; flesh white, thick, firm, without special odor.

114. Wine Red Stropharia   *Stropharia rugoso-annulata*

Gills: white at first, then grayish violet, finally blackish violet with white edges, notched where they touch the stem, thin, close.

Stem: white or pale yellowish, stout, smooth, dry; ring conspicuous, thick, with upper surface deeply radially grooved, lower part thick and feltlike, split into several radiating clawlike points that project beyond the upper part.

WHEN AND WHERE FOUND

Most often in fall, but may appear in spring or summer in areas that are frequently watered; on cultivated ground (flower beds, vegetable gardens, compost heaps, lawns).

REMARKS

Edible and choice. The wine-red cap and intricately constructed ring with its clawlike points are distinctive. Faded caps are strikingly different in color from those that have not faded. The occurrence of this mushroom only in cultivated areas may indicate that it is not a native species.

CLUSTERED WOODLOVER
Naematoloma fasciculare (purple-brown spores)

COLOR AND DESCRIPTION

Cap: orange-yellow or greenish yellow, first rounded, at length flat, turning olive green when rain-soaked, two to three inches across; flesh yellowish, very bitter.

Gills: at first yellow, then becoming green, finally purplish.

Stem: yellow, often twisted because of the dense, clustered growth.

WHEN AND WHERE FOUND

Fall, occasionally in spring or winter, on dead trees or stumps everywhere in the forest or along the edge of woodlands.

REMARKS

This mushroom, most attractive in looks, is now classed as

115. Clustered Woodlover   *Naematoloma fasciculare*

116. Smoky-gilled Woodlover   *Naematoloma capnoides*

poisonous. However, its exceedingly bitter taste, not lost in cooking, will deter the gatherer.

SMOKY-GILLED WOODLOVER
Naematoloma capnoides (purple-brown spores)

COLOR AND DESCRIPTION   [Color plate XXIV

    Cap: ocher-yellow, moist but not viscid, rounded then flat, two to three inches across; flesh whitish, quite firm, taste mild.

    Gills: smoky gray, touching the stem.

    Stem: white, becoming darker at the base, showing a few traces of the veil.

WHEN AND WHERE FOUND

    Early to late fall, on decaying logs in the forest, in clusters or in rows.

117. Rosy Gomphidius   *Gomphidius subroseus*

REMARKS

Edible and distinguished from the bitter, green-gilled wood-lover, *Naematoloma fasciculare,* by the smoky gray gills, as well as the lack of a bitter taste. It is rarely abundant until near the end of the season, and often continues to appear after cold weather has discouraged most other fungi.

ROSY GOMPHIDIUS
Gomphidius subroseus (blackish brown spores)

COLOR AND DESCRIPTION   [Color plate XXV]

Cap: rose-pink, rounded then spreading, surface covered by a thick, gelatinlike covering, slimy when wet, two to four inches across; flesh white.

Gills: whitish, then gray, soft and waxy, running down the stem.

Stem: white, two to three inches in length, yellow at the tapering base.

Fall, on the ground, often in moss or on the edges of Douglas fir forests.

REMARKS

This easily identified mushroom grows prolifically in many parts of the Puget Sound region and also at low elevations in the Cascade and Olympic mountains. The gelatinous covering is easily stripped from the caps. Although considered a choice edible mushroom by some, in reality it does not have much flavor. A very similar species, the Oregon gomphidius (*Gomphidius oregonensis*) is distinguished from the rosy gomphidius by its dingy grayish lilac, instead of rose-colored, cap, and its smaller spores. It is also edible.

WOOLLY GOMPHIDIUS
Chroogomphus (Gomphidius) tomentosus (black spores)

COLOR AND DESCRIPTION

Cap: orange or orange-buff, rounded or flat, *dry,* felted or finely and densely woolly, two to three inches broad; flesh orange-buff, thin, soft, without odor.

Gills: pale orange then gray or grayish orange from the spores, running down the stem, thick, distant.

Stem: orange or orange-buff, slender, dry, dull, felted below like the cap surface, about as long as the width of the cap.

WHEN AND WHERE FOUND

Fall, in conifer woods, especially in the mountains. Abundant in some seasons, difficult to find in others.

REMARKS

This is a characteristic mushroom of the Pacific Northwestern montane conifer forests. The dry, felted, orange cap

118. Woolly Gomphidius   *Chroogomphus (Gomphidius) tomentosus*

distinguishes it from all others of its tribe. Purple stains sometimes develop in older specimens. Although it certainly must
have been tried at one time or another, we have no authentic
reports on its edibility.

COLORFUL GOMPHIDIUS
Chroogomphus (Gomphidius) rutilus (black spores)

COLOR AND DESCRIPTION   [Color plate XXV]

Cap: olive brown or winy brown or tawny, sometimes
orange-ocher, often wine red in old specimens, convex, sometimes bluntly pointed in the center, smooth, sticky but not
slimy, soon dry and shining, two to three inches broad; flesh
pale orange, thick, without special taste or odor.

Gills: buff to yellowish brown or cinnamon brown at first,
soon gray from the spores, running down the stem.

Stem: buff or orange-buff, becoming wine red in age,
longer than the width of the cap, tapering at the base.

119. Colorful Gomphidius   *Chroogomphus (Gomphidius) rutilus*

WHEN AND WHERE FOUND

Fall, on the ground under lodgepole or ponderosa pine, sometimes also other conifers.

REMARKS

Edible. The slightly sticky cap and the mixtures of orange, buff, wine-red, and brown colors are distinctive.

SHAGGY MANE

Coprinus comatus (black spores)

COLOR AND DESCRIPTION   [Color plate XXVI]

Cap: white and gray covered with fluffy scales, standing erect like a closed umbrella on its handle, spreading with age, four to twelve inches in height; flesh white at first, then darkening.

Gills: white shading to pink, in flat folds against the stem, turning black with spores and melting into a black fluid.

Stem: white, hollow with small movable ring, slightly thicker at the base, four to ten inches in length.

WHEN AND WHERE FOUND

Spring or fall after rain; in the open, on the ground, in gravel by roadsides, near garbage dumps, or in decaying sawdust near old logging roads.

REMARKS

A well-known, edible mushroom of good flavor and consistency if gathered when young. Easily distinguished from the similar inky cap by its height and fluffy scales.

120. Shaggy Mane   *Coprinus comatus*

121. Inky Cap   *Coprinus atramentarius*

INKY CAP
Coprinus atramentarius (black spores)

COLOR AND DESCRIPTION   [Color plate XXVI]

Cap: lead gray or grayish tan, oval with depressed lines on the surface, two to four inches in width; flesh tannish white.

Gills: grayish, soon melting into black fluid.

Stem: white, hollow, splitting.

WHEN AND WHERE FOUND

Spring or fall, on the ground, densely clustered, often on edge of roads or fields, sometimes on lawns.

REMARKS

Edible but not as good as the shaggy mane. Only very young specimens should be gathered for food. Some people suffer digestive disturbances if they drink liquor while eating inky caps.

SHINY CAP
Coprinus micaceus (black spores)

COLOR AND DESCRIPTION

Cap: brownish tan to ocher-yellow, oval with lines on edge, later spreading, two to three inches wide; flesh whitish, thin.

Gills: grayish white, soon black with spores.

Stem: white, fragile, hollow, three to four inches in length.

WHEN AND WHERE FOUND

Spring and fall, at the base of old trees or from decayed wood underground, usually in the open.

REMARKS

Small mushroom, but has an excellent flavor in sauces. It is called "shiny cap" because the mealy particles on the cap are supposed to glisten like mica.

122. Shiny Cap   *Coprinus micaceus*

BELL-SHAPED PANAEOLUS
Panaeolus campanulatus (black spores)

COLOR AND DESCRIPTION

Cap: lead gray or brown, thin, bell-shaped, particles of the veil often adhering to the edge of the cap, one to two inches in width; flesh grayish, thin.

Gills: grayish, mottled with black spores.

Stem: gray, slender, two to five inches in length.

WHEN AND WHERE FOUND

Spring and fall, usually on dung or in rich pasture soil.

REMARKS

It is not likely that the collector will be tempted by this mushroom, but it has been experimented with. It is often confused with similar species which produce a peculiar type of intoxication.

HAYMAKER'S PANAEOLUS
Panaeolus foenisecii (black or very dark blackish brown spores)

COLOR AND DESCRIPTION

Cap: dull cinnamon brown or dull grayish brown with slight purplish cast when moist, fading to dingy buff with lilac tinge on drying, bell-shaped, moist but not viscid, smooth or sometimes a little wrinkled, one-half to three-quarters inch broad; flesh pale beige, thin, fragile, with "mushroomy" odor.

Gills: pallid or brownish pallid, then dark and somewhat mottled with the spores, broad, rounded where they touch the stem.

Stem: pale toward the top, dingy brown below, very slender, rigid, fragile, hollow, smooth, longer than the width of the cap.

123. Bell-shaped Panaeolus   *Panaeolus campanulatus*

124. Haymaker's Panaeolus   *Panaeolus foenisecii*

Spring and fall, in lawns and other open grassy places, always associated with grasses. May appear in the summer on well-watered lawns.

REMARKS

Edible, but not recommended. This, along with *Marasmius oreades, Entoloma sericeum,* and *Clitocybe dealbata,* is one of our common lawn-inhabiting mushrooms. Its brownish, bell-shaped cap, long, rigid, fragile stem, and black spores distinguish it.

Puffballs

Puffballs are a type of mushroom whose characteristics are soon learned and easily recognized by the beginner. There are several types of them, most of which are good to eat, and safe if certain precautions are observed. Always cut them in half lengthwise and look for any signs of gills being formed, which would indicate that you have the "button stage" of a gilled mushroom, possibly an Amanita. Also make sure that the interior tissue is uniformly white, discarding any with even a slight tinge of yellow. This discoloration means that the tissue has begun to decompose and will be altered in flavor and will possibly cause illness if eaten.

GIANT PUFFBALL

Calvatia gigantea (olive-brown spores)

COLOR AND DESCRIPTION

A large, white, rounded mass growing directly from the ground, the outer surface at first smooth, like fine kid leather, then cracking into flat plaques and coming off in pieces from the top down as the spores mature; flesh white when young, growing gradually yellow, then dark brown with the ripening of the spores; often one to two feet in diameter, one to thirty pounds in weight.

WHEN AND WHERE FOUND

Spring or fall, in rich grounds near barns or in pastures, always in the open.

REMARKS

A fine edible mushroom. Eat it while the flesh is pure white; a tinge of yellow means a bitter taste. Other smaller

125. Giant Puffball   *Calvatia gigantea*

puffballs (*Lycoperdon perlatum*) are edible when young and pure white within. Slice puffballs through the center to be sure you have not picked the button of an Amanita. If you have, signs of the stem and cap will be seen, while in the puffball there is only solid white flesh.

WARTED GIANT PUFFBALL
Calbovista subsculpta (yellow-brown to olive-brown spores)

COLOR AND DESCRIPTION

White, the outer surface from the first cracked into large, coarse warts like pyramids with their tops cut off, about half an inch wide at their bases and nearly as high, pear-shaped or globose, about three to six inches in diameter; flesh white, turning yellow then dark olive brown as the spores mature, firm.

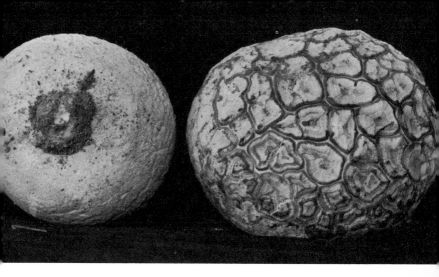

126. Warted Giant Puffball *Calbovista subsculpta*

WHEN AND WHERE FOUND

Spring or fall, on the ground under conifers in the mountains, usually under ponderosa pine on the eastern slope of the Cascade Mountains.

REMARKS

Edible, and much sought after in some parts of the Pacific Northwest. Its coarsely warted outer surface easily distinguishes it from the giant puffball, but not so readily from the Sierran puffball, which is also coarsely warted. There the distinction is a microscopical one, having to do with the thread-like material (capillitium) in the meshes of which the spores are found.

SIERRAN PUFFBALL
Calvatia sculpta (yellow-brown spores)

COLOR AND DESCRIPTION

White, covered with long, sharp-pointed, narrowly pyramidal warts up to an inch long, arising one to several from

127. Sierran Puffball   *Calvatia sculpta*

angular plaques into which the outer wall has cracked and which fall away one by one, revealing the dusty mass of spores, pear-shaped, two to four inches broad; flesh white at first, firm.

128. Broad Puffball   *Lycoperdon perlatum*

Summer or early fall, under conifers at high elevations in the mountains of the West Coast.

REMARKS

This spectacularly spiny puffball is usually found by those who are exploring mountain trails at elevations of around 6,000 to 7,000 feet. It looks something like the warted giant puffball, but its spines are much longer and sharper. The most reliable difference between them is a microscopical one (see the remarks under *Calbovista subsculpta*).

BROAD PUFFBALL
Lycoperdon perlatum (olive-brown spores)

COLOR AND DESCRIPTION

White or pale dingy cream or pale dingy brownish, more or less pear-shaped, about three to four inches tall, one to two inches wide at the top, with a pore at the top through which the spores escape, often with a rather long, stemlike base, covered all over with short, conical or pyramidal spines that break off readily, leaving a smooth spot; flesh white, then greenish yellow, then olive brown.

Fall, in woods of various kinds, also in lawns or on cultivated ground.

Edible and of good quality as long as the flesh is pure white. This is one of the Pacific Northwest's commonest puffballs, easily recognized by its long, stemlike base and short spines that fall off.

CLUSTERED PUFFBALL
Lycoperdon pyriforme (olive-brown spores)

Some shade of brown on the upper portion, white at the base, which is fastened to white, stringlike strands of mycelium, about two or two and a half inches tall, one inch or so broad at the top, covered with small granules giving the surface a rough feel; flesh white, then greenish yellow, finally olive brown.

Fall, in dense, compact clusters, often of dozens of individuals, on rotten wood or at the base of stumps, in conifer or mixed forests.

Edible and choice if young and firm and flesh is pure white. The crowded clusters of brown, pear-shaped puffballs make this species easy to recognize.

129. Clustered Puffball   *Lycoperdon pyriforme*

THICK-SKINNED PUFFBALLS
Scleroderma (blackish brown or blackish violet spores)

COLOR AND DESCRIPTION   [Color plate XXVII]

Dingy yellowish or dingy brown, with white, stringlike strands of mycelium attached to the base, globose, sometimes lobed or irregular, surface smooth or cracked into small, irregular plaques, the "rind" or spore case thick, hard, finally cracking open in an irregular manner; flesh white in very young specimens, but soon turning grayish violet then blackish violet, somewhat mottled, eventually becoming a violet-black or blackish brown powder, firm, hard, not spongy.

WHEN AND WHERE FOUND

Fall, sometimes also in spring, on the ground or sometimes partly buried, in woods, along paths, also in gardens, flower beds, or under cultivated shrubs.

REMARKS

To be avoided; the taste of most Sclerodermas is said to be disagreeable, and some persons are made ill by them. The several *Scleroderma* species of the Pacific Northwest are not

130. Thick-skinned Puffballs *Scleroderma*

well understood, but they have some general features in common that make them fairly easy to recognize. One of these features is the thick, hard, persistent rind or outer wall, and another is the purplish color assumed by the flesh at an early stage. The flesh is hard and solid, not spongy like that of the Lycoperdons, and looks mottled when the purple color develops.

Polypores

Polypores resemble boletes in having tubes instead of gills on the undersurface of the cap, but most of them are stemless and grow shelflike, attached to wood by the side of the cap. Most are too tough to eat, or have a disagreeable flavor, so the group as a whole is not of very much interest to the mushroom eater. The few that resemble boletes because of being soft and fleshy, growing on the ground, and having an umbrellalike cap and stem can be recognized as polypores by their white to cream-colored spore print.

CHICKEN-OF-THE-WOODS
Polyporus sulphureus (white spores)

COLOR AND DESCRIPTION   [Color plate XXVII]

Cap: orange to red, in wide-spreading brackets or shelves attached by the side of the cap to the tree trunk or log, almost stemless, often growing in dense series, four to six inches across, in many layers; flesh white, unchanging when bruised, odor strongly musky, somewhat acidulous in age.

Pores: clear sulphur yellow, unchanging in color if bruised.

Stem: slight or lacking, the brackets growing directly from the host. Hundreds may grow on one log or tree.

WHEN AND WHERE FOUND

Late summer and fall, on rotting logs or stumps, occasionally from a wound in a live tree. Sometimes the mycelium may live in a log many years before fruiting bodies appear, then fruit on the same log for several seasons.

131. Chicken-of-the-Woods   *Polyporus sulphureus*

REMARKS

A brilliant sight to come on unexpectedly in the woods.

132. Kurotake   *Polyporus leucomelas*

When young the margin is tender and makes an excellent dish. The soft, cheesy consistency makes this polypore quite different from other bracket-shaped mushrooms seen in the woods.

KUROTAKE
Polyporus leucomelas (pallid grayish spores)

COLOR AND DESCRIPTION

Cap: at first white or very pale gray, soon becoming very dark brownish black, rounded, smooth, three to six inches broad; flesh white, thick, firm, without special odor.

Pores: white, running down the stem, small, very shallow.

Stem: white then pale gray, stout, solid, hard-fleshed, dry, dull, no longer than the width of the cap.

WHEN AND WHERE FOUND

Fall, on the ground under conifers, mostly in mountainous areas.

POLYPORES   *171*

Edible, but has a bitter taste that requires special treatment. The Japanese method is to soak the mushroom for a long time in brine, whereupon the bitter taste disappears, but the fungus turns black (*kurotake* means "black mushroom") and presents a rather discouraging aspect for something that is supposed to be eaten.

Spine Fungi

Most of the edible spine fungi grow on the ground and resemble gilled mushrooms or boletes, with umbrellalike or funnel-shaped cap and stem, but the undersurface of the cap is covered with small, downward-pointing spines instead of gills or tubes. Another type grows on wood and consists of a mass of fleshy branches ending in downward-directed spines. The group is easily recognized and contains at least two well-liked edible species, as well as several that are either too tough or too unpleasantly flavored to be eaten.

SPREADING-HEDGEHOG MUSHROOM
Dentinum (Hydnum) repandum (white spores)

COLOR AND DESCRIPTION   [Color plate XXVIII]

Cap: cream or tan, smooth or slightly scaly, first rounded then spreading and irregular, two to four inches across; flesh white, soft and brittle.

Spines: white or buff, small and tender.

Stem: white, sometimes central, occasionally to one side of center, two to three inches in length.

WHEN AND WHERE FOUND

Fall, on the ground, most frequently at low elevations in conifer forests of the Olympic and Cascade mountains.

REMARKS

A good edible mushroom, considered by some as good as the chanterelle. It resembles the chanterelle in appearance, but the spines on the lower surface make it unmistakable.

133. Spreading-Hedgehog Mushroom   *Dentinum (Hydnum) repandum*

SCALY HYDNUM
Hydnum imbricatum (dull brown spores)

COLOR AND DESCRIPTION

Cap: dull brown with purplish tinge, the scales often darker, convex then flattened and more or less hollowed in the center, covered with coarse scales with free tips, three to six inches broad; flesh pale grayish buff, thick, pale, taste mild or slightly of fresh meal.

Spines: pale grayish brown with lilac tinge, becoming darker brown, pointed, soft, running down the stem slightly sometimes, about one-quarter to one-half inch long.

Stem: pale grayish buff, sometimes more brownish, stout, tapering at the base, shorter than the width of the cap.

WHEN AND WHERE FOUND

Fall, on the ground in conifer woods.

Edible, but should be tried cautiously, as some persons are made ill by it. Only young specimens should be used. A similar species, the rough-capped hydnum (*Hydnum scabrosum*), has a blackish green stem base and a very bitter taste. It is not edible.

PECK'S HYDNUM
Hydnellum peckii (fawn-brown spores)

COLOR AND DESCRIPTION

Cap: dark brown in the center, pale salmon pink on the margin, flat or slightly depressed in the center, surface often covered with coarse nodules, felty or woolly, exuding drops of blood-red liquid in wet weather, three to six inches broad;

134. Scaly Hydnum   *Hydnum imbricatum*

135. Peck's Hydnum *Hydnellum peckii*

flesh brown, thick, corky, fibrous, tough, with sweet, aromatic odor and intensely peppery taste.

Spines: pale dingy salmon pink at first, then brown, very slender, about a quarter of an inch long.

Stem: dark brown, felty or finely woolly, one to three inches tall.

WHEN AND WHERE FOUND

Fall, on the ground under conifers, usually in dense conifer woods. Abundant in some seasons, not common in others.

REMARKS

Inedible; the flesh is very tough and fibrous. The colors, fibrous flesh, red drops of liquid on the cap (when present), sweet odor, and very peppery taste make this an easily recognized fungus.

CORAL HYDNUM
Hericium coralloides (colorless spores, white in mass)

COLOR AND DESCRIPTION

White or cream-white, whole plant consisting of a mass of branches coming from a common center, dividing again into branchlets which are covered with stalactitelike spines hanging from them. The young plants are compact, soon spreading into large clusters from a few inches to two or more feet wide and a foot or more in length as they hang from tree or log.

Spines: white or creamy, one-quarter to one-half inch long.

136. Coral Hydnum   *Hericium coralloides*

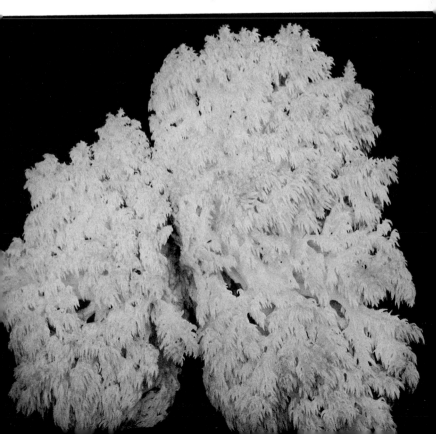

Late summer through fall, in old Douglas fir forests on fallen logs, stumps, or old trees.

REMARKS

Edible and considered very good by most people. Not too much should be eaten at one time, as the larger branches are somewhat stringy and may prove indigestible. This beautiful, impressive mushroom, often reaching a very large size, could not be confused with anything poisonous and so is one of the safest for the beginner to look for and try.

Coral Fungi

The mushrooms in this group consist of masses of erect, fleshy branches, hence the popular name "coral." Avoid those in which the flesh in the base of the plant is rubbery and translucent, like stiff gelatin. If this precaution is observed, the various corals can be sampled with little fear of bad consequences—subject, of course, to the standard rule of always trying any new mushroom in small quantity for the first time.

Probably the names by which we have known some of the corals of the Pacific Northwest for years will have to be changed eventually. More detailed investigation by experts on coral fungi seems to show that many of the western species are not quite like those of the same name in the eastern United States or Europe. In the meantime, until the experts make their pronouncements, the customary names will serve our purpose very well.

CAULIFLOWER MUSHROOM
Sparassis radicata (white spores)

COLOR AND DESCRIPTION

Cream-white mass consisting of ribbonlike branches arising from a single, long, pointed base. Consistency firm, odor pleasant, six inches to three feet across, weight up to forty pounds.

WHEN AND WHERE FOUND

Fall, in conifer forests, base attached to the root of a tree.

REMARKS

This large, remarkable-looking mushroom growth is one of the best of the edible species. Cauliflower mushrooms will

137. Cauliflower Mushroom   *Sparassis radicata*

fruit several years from the same base if the base is left in the ground. Cut the mushroom off at ground level; do not pull it up.

CRESTED CORAL
Clavulina (Clavaria) cristata (white spores)

COLOR AND DESCRIPTION

White, dingy ivory, pale gray, or tinged with violet, many slender branches from a stemlike base, the branches toothed or crested at their tips, often irregular and somewhat flattened, three or four inches tall, taste and odor mild.

WHEN AND WHERE FOUND

Fall, in the ground in conifer woods.

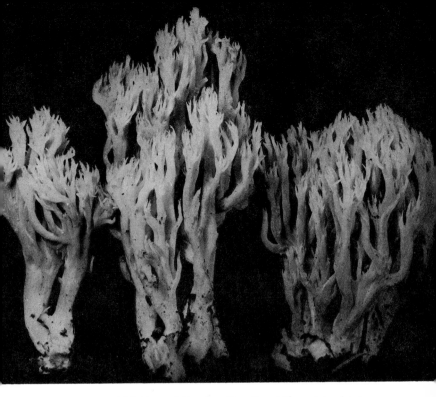

138. Crested Coral   *Clavulina (Clavaria) cristata*

REMARKS

Edible and considered excellent by many. One of the Pacific Northwest's commonest coral fungi, often making up in numbers what it lacks in size. The gray form and the purplish or lavender form are sometimes given separate names, but the colors seem to grade into one another so that it would often be hard to make distinctions on color alone. This coral is often parasitized by another fungus that turns it black and makes it thicker and knobby. These parasitized specimens should be discarded when collecting for the table.

PURPLE-TIPPED CORAL

Ramaria (Clavaria) botrytis (yellow spores)

COLOR AND DESCRIPTION   [Color plate XXVIII]

Branches white, tipped with purple rose or red; many branches from one base, dividing into branchlets; from two to five inches in height.

WHEN AND WHERE FOUND

Fall, on the ground, usually in moss, in old Douglas fir forests.

REMARKS

A very beautiful mushroom. It is edible and considered by many to be the best tasting of all the large corals. In the young stage it is easily recognized, with its massive, fleshy white base and multitude of short, stubby branches with knobby, reddish or purplish tips. When the branches lengthen and the color fades somewhat, it has a more ordinary appearance.

YELLOW CORAL

Ramaria (Clavaria) flava (yellow spores)

COLOR AND DESCRIPTION   [Color plate XXIX]

Cream-yellow to rather bright yellow, much branched, the tips of the branchlets yellow also, from four to ten inches across; flesh white, soft, *not gelatinous,* odor and taste mild.

WHEN AND WHERE FOUND

Late summer and fall, in conifer forests, sometimes on well-rotted logs.

REMARKS

There are several kinds of coral that grow on rotten logs. Some of them are buff or dull yellow in color and resemble

139. Purple-tipped Coral   *Ramaria (Clavaria) botrytis*

140. Yellow Coral   *Ramaria (Clavaria) flava*

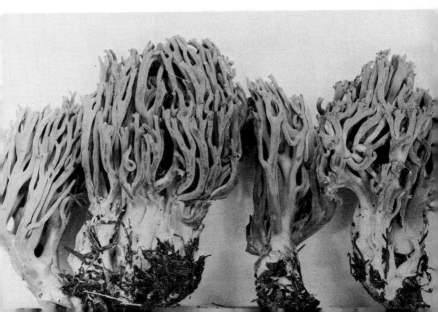

141. Formosa Coral   *Ramaria (Clavaria) formosa*

the yellow coral in appearance. They are usually tough and stringy, and often have a bitter or astringent taste. These are members of the *Ramaria stricta* group, which in general are inedible because of the taste and consistency mentioned. There are several soft-fleshed yellow Ramarias in the Puget Sound region, distinguished from one another by microscopical features that are of no interest to the mushroom eater. They all go under the name of *Ramaria* (or *Clavaria*) *flava*, which might not satisfy the scientist, but is perfectly acceptable to the layman.

FORMOSA CORAL
Ramaria (Clavaria) formosa (yellow spores)

COLOR AND DESCRIPTION

Salmon pink to rosy pink, the tips of the branches yellow, six to twelve inches across; flesh of the branches of the fruiting body is white, pulpy, or fibrous, *not gelatinous.*

WHEN AND WHERE FOUND

Fall, rarely in the spring, under conifers on the ground in forests throughout the Puget Sound area, also in the Cascade and Olympic mountains.

REMARKS

Very similar in color and general appearance to the gelatinous coral, but lacks its rubbery, gelatinous flesh. If salmon-pink or creamy pink corals are collected for the table, the flesh of *every specimen* must be examined to be sure that no gelatinous coral is included. It would be well to sample the formosa coral cautiously the first time, since people are apt to differ in their reactions to this fungus. See gelatinous coral.

GELATINOUS CORAL
Ramaria (Clavaria) gelatinosa (ocher spores)

COLOR AND DESCRIPTION   [Color plate XXIX]

Cream or pinkish cinnamon, many-branched cluster, often

142. Gelatinous Coral   *Ramaria (Clavaria) gelatinosa*

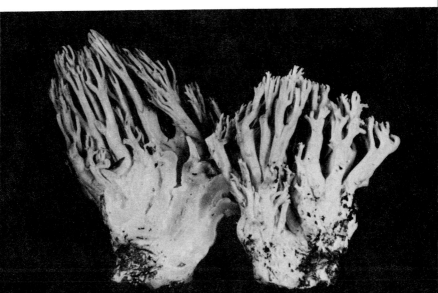

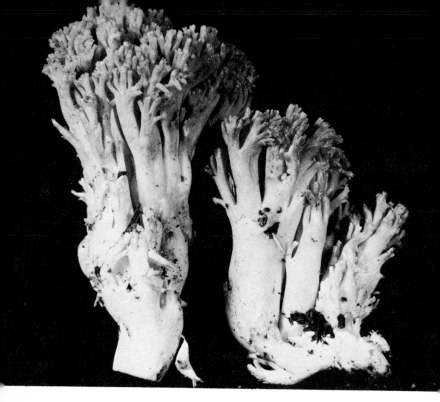

143. Rose Coral   *Ramaria (Clavaria) subbotrytis*

with yellowish branch tips, six to twelve inches in width. When a cluster is cut through the center, it shows semitransparent flesh of gelatinous consistency.

WHEN AND WHERE FOUND

Fall, in old Douglas fir forests.

REMARKS

This coral has been classed as poisonous by many collectors. Every specimen of coral which has been collected by the hunter should be carefully cut through the middle and all those showing a gelatinous flesh should be discarded.

ROSE CORAL
Ramaria (Clavaria) subbotrytis (pinkish buff spores)

A begonia-rose or geranium-pink fruiting body, six to twelve inches across, the numerous branches growing from a large, central white base, and all having the intense rose-pink coloration, fading in age to salmon pink, bland taste and no odor.

WHEN AND WHERE FOUND

Late fall, in old, unlogged Douglas fir forests at low elevations in the Cascade and Olympic mountains, on the ground.

REMARKS

One of the most beautiful of the coral mushrooms. Care should be taken to collect young, fresh specimens. Always cut through the base in order to distinguish it from the poisonous gelatinous coral.

Jelly Fungi

These curious mushrooms are, as their name suggests, of a consistency like stiff, rubbery gelatin, or sometimes very soft gelatin. They adorn our forests with a variety of colors and interesting forms, but do not have much to offer to the mushroom eater. None is known to be poisonous, but they have little or no flavor and their peculiar texture does not appeal to everyone. If cooked, they melt, leaving only thin membranes, so one must eat them raw, pickled, or marinated.

WITCH'S BUTTER
Dacrymyces palmatus (orange-yellow spores)

COLOR AND DESCRIPTION   [Color plate XXX]

Growing from wood as a bright orange, lobed, irregular mass one-half to one or two inches broad, firm and rubbery at first, but soon becoming soft, and often melting into a soupy mass when old.

WHEN AND WHERE FOUND

Late fall, sometimes continuing into winter if the weather is not too severe; on wood, in practically any kind of forest.

REMARKS

This is one of the Pacific Northwest's commonest jelly fungi, usually not appearing in any abundance until the weather has become decidedly cool, in late fall. The fruiting bodies might make a colorful addition to a green salad, but otherwise would seem to have little appeal to the palate. Only young specimens are firm enough to be considered for eating.

WHITE JELLY MUSHROOM
Pseudohydnum gelatinosum
(colorless spores, white in mass)

COLOR AND DESCRIPTION   [Color plate XXXI]

Cap: translucent white, sometimes shaded gray, gelatinous, erect on twigs or attached by the side on decaying logs, minute spines on the under- or spore-bearing surface, one to three inches in height or width.

WHEN AND WHERE FOUND

Fall after heavy rains, in Douglas fir forests.

REMARKS

A very beautiful little mushroom. It is of slight value for food, but may be eaten raw with sugar and cream, or marinated in French dressing and used in salad.

144. Witch's Butter   *Dacrymyces palmatus*

145. White Jelly Mushroom *Pseudohydnum gelatinosum*

146. Apricot Jelly Mushroom *Phlogiotis helvelloides*

APRICOT JELLY MUSHROOM

Phlogiotis helvelloides (colorless spores, white in mass)

COLOR AND DESCRIPTION   [Color plate XXXI]

Apricot or salmon color, often fading to pale orange, gelatinous, somewhat funnel-shaped or like a little calla lily, surface smooth, one to three inches in height.

WHEN AND WHERE FOUND

Late summer and fall, in damp ground on rotting wood, under Douglas firs.

REMARKS

May be pickled in vinegar, candied in sugar syrup, or eaten raw in salads.

Cup Fungi,
Helvellas, Morels

In this type of mushroom the spores are produced in a tiny, club-shaped cell, the ascus (plural, asci), from which they are shot out with considerable force when mature. Hundreds of thousands of these tiny asci will be packed closely together side by side to make up the spore-bearing surface of a cup fungus of ordinary size. When a mature cup is picked, it may well happen that a slight jar or a slight change in humidity of the air will cause several thousand asci to discharge their spores at the same time. The spores are shot into the air and carried up by air currents, appearing like a little cloud of steam rising from the cup. If the room is very still, one may even hear a faint hissing sound when the "puffing" takes place.

As with other groups of mushrooms, different people may have different reactions to the same species within this group, hence an unfamiliar species should be tried in *small quantity* for the first time. Several of the large cup fungi and helvellas have toxic materials that are broken down by heat, so that the fungus is rendered safe by thorough cooking. From this it follows that cup fungi and their allies should not be eaten raw.

ORANGE FAIRY CUP
Aleuria aurantia (whitish spores)

COLOR AND DESCRIPTION   [Color plate XXXII]

Brilliant orange, cup-shaped, growing scattered or clustered, margin first inrolled, expanding into the cup shape.

147. Orange Fairy Cup   *Aleuria aurantia*

WHEN AND WHERE FOUND

In the fall, less abundantly in spring; on the ground, in the open, often along newly graded roads or along logging roads.

REMARKS

Edible and pleasant-tasting. Although there is very little substance to the caps, the quantity in which these orange cups can be gathered may make them worth while.

VIOLET STAR CUP
Sarcosphaera eximia (pale yellowish spores)

COLOR AND DESCRIPTION

Growing as a hollow sphere, two to four inches in diameter, just below the surface of the ground, then barely breaking the surface and splitting into pointed segments that open out in a starlike manner, outer surface white, but usually dingy from adhering soil, inner spore-bearing surface white at first, then a beautiful shade of violet.

CUP FUNGI, HELVELLAS, MORELS   *193*

148. Violet Star Cup *Sarcosphaera eximia*

Fall, sometimes also spring, on the ground in sandy or soft soil. In the Pacific Northwest it grows under conifers, but in other areas it may appear under hardwoods.

REMARKS

A beautiful mushroom when well developed, with its petal-like lobes and violet lining of the cup. It seems particularly partial to sandy soil under pines along the eastern slope of the Cascade Mountains. As an edible mushroom it leaves something to be desired; it is definitely poisonous to some persons, and even if such is not the case, most specimens would be difficult to rid of the soil that clings to their outer surface.

ELFIN SADDLE
Helvella lacunosa (whitish spores)

COLOR AND DESCRIPTION

Cap: white or blackish gray, thin skin folded in saddle shape.

Stem: white or shaded gray, grooved with longitudinal depressions.

Fall after heavy rains, on the ground in Douglas fir forests, or older thickets, or along the margins of patches of bracken.

149. Elfin Saddle   *Helvella lacunosa*

Although the flavor is similar to that of the morel, great care should be taken in testing this mushroom. Gather only fresh, young specimens, as old specimens develop poisonous characteristics. They should never be tasted raw and should be blanched in boiling water before cooking. Observe the precaution of trying a small quantity before eating any large amount.

BRAIN MUSHROOM
Gyromitra esculenta (yellowish spores)

COLOR AND DESCRIPTION

Cap: dark reddish-brown, rounded, folded into many convolutions, like the lobes of the brain, not pitted with distinct depressions as is the morel, three to four inches across.

Stem: white or brownish, the cap attached near the top, smooth, often grooved, two to three inches in length.

WHEN AND WHERE FOUND

Spring and summer, under various types of trees or in the open; often near garbage dumps.

REMARKS

If young, firm, brown specimens are used, the brain mushroom can be eaten by most persons. Avoid blackened, soft, or withered caps, which may have begun to decompose. If you want to be extra cautious, parboil the mushrooms and discard the water. This fungus has had a dubious reputation as an esculent for some time, and with good reason, because in Europe it is known to have caused many serious cases of poisoning and several fatalities. No fatalities, and relatively few cases of poisoning, have been recorded in North America from its use. Every year very many people eat the local "race" that grows in the Puget Sound country and the Cascade Mountains, with no reported cases of poisoning so far. Whether this would be true for other regions of the West Coast is not

150. Brain Mushroom   *Gyromitra esculenta*

151. Hooded Helvella   *Gyromitra infula*

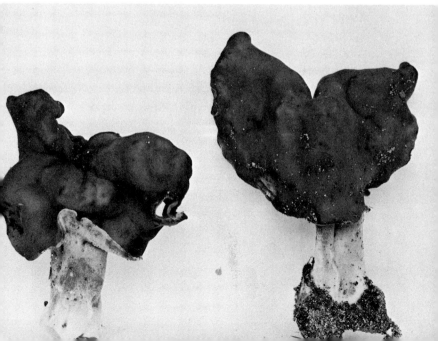

certain. In any case, if you try the brain mushroom, do not eat large quantities of it, and do not eat it several days in succession.

HOODED HELVELLA
Gyromitra infula (whitish spores)

COLOR AND DESCRIPTION

Cap: cinnamon or dark brown, thin skin folded into a saddle shape, two to three inches across.

Stem: light purplish brown, usually smooth, sometimes grooved or folded.

WHEN AND WHERE FOUND

Late summer and fall, occasionally in the spring, on rotten wood or on old logs in the forest.

REMARKS

The edibility of the hooded helvella, like that of the brain mushroom, is questioned so it is better not to experiment. Never taste this mushroom raw.

GIANT HELVELLA
Gyromitra gigas (whitish spores)

COLOR AND DESCRIPTION   [Color plate XXXII]

Cap: ocher-yellow or tan, sometimes darker brown, folded into many convolutions, four to nine inches across.

Stem: white, longitudinally ridged and folded, nearly as thick as the cap, often nearly or quite hidden by the margin of the cap which comes down over it almost to the ground; whole plant often weighs one to two pounds.

WHEN AND WHERE FOUND

Spring, or early summer, on the ground under conifers, sometimes near melting snowfields.

152. Giant Helvella *Gyromitra gigas*

REMARKS

Edible, and considered excellent by most people. Care should be taken to distinguish it from the brain mushroom and the hooded helvella. In cooking the giant helvella, first parboil and throw away the water in which it was blanched, rinse the pieces, then proceed with the cooking. Eat only a small quantity on first trial.

CALIFORNIA ELFIN SADDLE
Gyromitra californica (whitish spores)

COLOR AND DESCRIPTION

Cap: tan to olive brown in undulating folds, sometimes saddle-shaped, at other times broad and rounded, edge inrolled, white beneath, two to four inches across.

Stem: white, fluted in wide, flat folds, three to four inches in height, stained rose at the base.

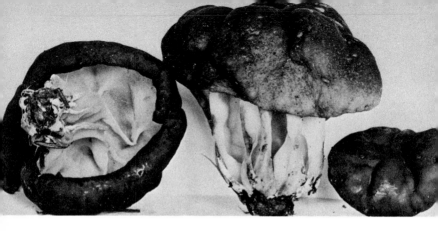

153. California Elfin Saddle   *Gyromitra californica*

154. Early Morel   *Verpa bohemica*

Usually in light soil in conifer woods, or along old logging roads and other open areas in the woods.

REMARKS

Little is known of the edibility of this species, and care should be taken in sampling it. Never taste it raw; parboil it and discard the water. Eat only a small quantity on first trial. Similar species are hooded helvella, brain mushroom, and giant helvella. The flanged, white stem with rose-colored base and the thin, membranelike brown cap are the features that characterize the California elfin saddle.

EARLY MOREL
Verpa bohemica (pale yellow spores)

COLOR AND DESCRIPTION

Cap: tan or brown, conspicuously wrinkled, thimble-shaped, hollow, lobed edge free from the stem, one to two inches across.

Stem: cream-white, long, hollow, often larger at base, three to five inches in length.

WHEN AND WHERE FOUND

Early spring, March through April, before the ordinary morel appears. It grows on the ground, often along riverbanks under cottonwoods, willows, and aspens, well hidden under dead leaves.

REMARKS

A widely known mushroom, not quite as good in flavor as the later morel. The long stems as well as the caps are edible. Some may prefer to parboil these mushrooms and discard the water in which they were boiled. Try a small quantity the first time, as some people are allergic to morels.

EDIBLE MOREL
Morchella esculenta (yellowish spores)

COLOR AND DESCRIPTION

Cap: pale brownish cream to pale brown or pale grayish brown, edges of the ridges not darker, oval in outline, or sometimes bluntly cone-shaped with rounded top, hollow, fastened to the stem at its lower edge, covered with rather deep pits, the ridges between pits running irregularly in all directions, about two to four inches tall and half as wide.

Stem: white or pallid, stout, hollow, straight or club-shaped or bulbous, finally granular all over, shorter than the cap.

WHEN AND WHERE FOUND

April, May, and sometimes into June, in deserted apple orchards, open fields, various kinds of woods, yards, gardens, and sometimes in recently burned areas, but not so commonly there, perhaps, as the narrow-capped morel.

REMARKS

One of the most highly prized of all edible mushrooms. A few unfortunate individuals have a bad reaction to morels, so if you have never eaten them, try cautiously at first. The two features supposed to characterize this particular species of morel are the light-colored, irregular ridges that do not run in vertical lines and the predominately oval cap. With these features well developed, it does indeed look different from the narrow-capped morel, but intergradations can be found. For the mushroom hunter, however, distinctions between the various species of morels are truly academic, all species being equally edible and delicious.

NARROW-CAPPED MOREL
Morchella angusticeps (yellowish spores)

COLOR AND DESCRIPTION

Cap: pits dull brown, ridges darker gray-brown or slate

155. Edible Morel *Morchella esculenta*

156. Narrow-capped Morel *Morchella angusticeps*

gray, often becoming almost black with age, in the shape of a narrow cone with bluntly rounded tip, hollow, fastened by the lower edge to the stem but with a pronounced groove before it touches the stem, ridges between pits running conspicuously in vertical lines, connected by cross ridges, two to four inches tall, about an inch wide, sometimes narrower.

Stem: dingy cream to buff, stout, often furrowed at the base, granular all over, shorter than the cap.

WHEN AND WHERE FOUND

April, May, and sometimes June, in much the same places as the edible morel. The narrow-capped morel is often to be found in some quantity under conifers and their understory of shrubs along the eastern slopes of the Cascade Mountains. The experienced morel hunter always searches very carefully those areas where a forest fire has occurred the preceding summer, as *Morchella angusticeps* (and other morels, for that matter) is often to be found there in abundance the first year, less the second, and still less or not at all thereafter.

REMARKS

Like all true morels, edible and delicious. The narrow, cone-shaped cap and the conspicuous vertical main ridges, darker in color than the pits between them, are the two main features of this morel.

Mushroom Poisons

By VARRO E. TYLER

ALTHOUGH the number of toxic mushrooms forms a comparatively small percentage of the total number of species, the types of poisons contained in this limited group are extremely variable. More accurate information on the chemistry and distribution of these different toxins has been obtained in the last two decades than in all of the time previous. Still, the most convenient basis for classifying them is by the nature of the effects they produce after having been eaten by human beings. Four basic types of mushroom toxins are ordinarily recognized: protoplasmic poisons, compounds affecting the nervous system, gastrointestinal irritants, and disulfiramlike constituents. Minor subvarieties of each of these main types also exist.

All of the known poisonous mushrooms contain principles with one or more of these activities. However, the picture is often complicated by differences in concentration of the poisonous principles in different collections of the same species, as well as by the variation in response that different individuals exhibit toward the same toxin. This simple classification does not include poisonings resulting from hypersensitivity (allergy) to mushroom protein or from the ingestion of mushrooms that have been decomposed by microbial action.

PROTOPLASMIC POISONS

Two basic kinds of protoplasmic poisons are known, an extremely poisonous mixture of toxins found in certain *Amanita* and *Galerina* species and a second, less active variety occurring in *Gyromitra esculenta*. The former compounds are designated as amanita toxins, regardless of the type of mushroom in which they are found, and the latter as gyromitrin. Amanita toxins occur in species of *Amanita* belonging to a closely related group of species including *A. phalloides, A. verna, A. virosa,* and *A. bisporigera* (so-called deadly Amanitas). Mushrooms of this group are very rare in the Pacific Northwest, but some have been reported in recent years. This scarcity would seem to indicate that they are not native species, probably having been introduced on the roots of trees with which they form mycorhizal associations. Amanita toxins also occur in *Galerina autumnalis, G. marginata,* and *G. venenata.* These species grow with some frequency in Washington and Oregon, but since they are relatively small and nondescript in appearance, they are seldom collected for table use.

The poisoning produced by either of these kinds of mushrooms containing amanita toxins is of the worst type, being insidious in onset and commonly fatal. It is characterized by a long latent period between the eating of the mushrooms and the appearance of symptoms. Ordinarily ten to twenty hours will pass and then, abruptly, violent vomiting and diarrhea begin and may continue until death results; or if the patient survives this phase through appropriate treatment, he may appear to be recovering for a short time, but generally relapses because of progressive injury to his liver, kidney, heart, and skeletal muscles, with death resulting after two to five days in at least 50 percent of the cases.

Persons suspected of having eaten such mushrooms should be hospitalized immediately and placed under the direct supervision of a physician. Treatment consists of removal of the toxic material from the gastrointestinal tract by administration of emetics and cathartics, gastric lavage, and enemas. Hemodialysis is indicated if possible, otherwise peritoneal dialysis may prove effective. Maintenance of electrolyte and fluid balance, which is crucial, will require a liquid diet of high carbohydrate and salt content; intravenous injection of dextrose solution four or five times daily may also be necessary. Additional treatment is symptomatic and supportive.

European physicians report that slow infusion of thioctic (α-lipoic) acid has proved effective as an antidote, but additional verification is required. The *sérum antiphallinique* prepared in France and allegedly effective in the treatment of amanita toxin poisoning is not ordinarily available in this country. A widely publicized treatment calling for the ingestion of chopped, raw rabbit stomach and brains is based on the false premise that rabbits are immune to amanita toxin poisoning and can scarcely be recommended for a person suffering severe nausea.

Gyromitrin, the second major type of protoplasmic poison, is less dangerous than the amanita toxins but still capable of producing fatal results. The compound has been isolated from a single species of false morel, *Gyomitra esculenta,* but probably also occurs in *Gyromitra gigas* and *Helvella underwoodii.* Because it is very volatile, false morels can be rendered edible by parboiling or long drying, but the irregular distribution of toxicity within the same species remains unexplained. European specimens of *Gyromitra esculenta* are almost uniformly toxic; cases of poisoning from the fungi collected in the eastern United States have been reported, but no single case of serious poisoning has been reliably reported from samples collected west of the Rocky Mountains. At present we can only conclude that different races of the species exist, some of which may contain little or no gyromitrin.

In any event, it is well known that severe, even fatal, cases of poisoning may arise from eating these false morels. As is the case with amanita toxins, there is a distinct, although somewhat shorter, latent period between the meal and the onset of symptoms. This period is rarely less than two hours and is more commonly six to eight hours. The symptoms are a feeling of fullness in the stomach followed by violent vomiting and watery diarrhea which may persist for one or two days. Headache, lassitude, cramps, and intense pain in the liver and gastric region are followed by jaundice. In severe cases, the patient undergoes general collapse, the pulse becomes irregular, breathing is difficult, and delirium and convulsions occur; death may result from liver damage or heart failure, usually within ten days.

Call a physician in any case of poisoning or suspected poisoning by *Gyromitra esculenta* or related false morels. Treatment is very similar to that described for the amanita toxins and includes gastric lavage, administration of cathartics, enemas, forced fluids, and possibly hemodialysis. Beyond this, care should be symptomatic and supportive.

SUBSTANCES AFFECTING THE NERVOUS SYSTEM

The compounds in mushrooms that have an effect on some portion of the nervous system may be classified into three chemical types: muscarine, ibotenic acid-muscimol, and psilocybin-psilocin. The latter two types of compounds influence the central nervous system, producing various effects, including hallucinations. Muscarine does not produce such symptoms, its action on the nervous system being strictly peripheral.

Muscarine

First isolated from *Amanita muscaria* approximately 150 years ago, muscarine derives its name from that species. It does occur in both *A. muscaria* and *A. pantherina* in relatively small amounts, but contrary to some older statements, it is not the principal toxic agent in those mushrooms. Certain species of *Clitocybe,* such as *C. dealbata,* and a large number of species of *Inocybe,* including *I. napipes, I. mixtilis,* and *I. pudica,* contain muscarine in considerable quantities and produce cases of poisoning with typical uncomplicated muscarine symptoms.

These symptoms appear quite rapidly after the mushrooms have been eaten, usually within fifteen to thirty minutes, beginning with greatly increased secretion of saliva, sweat, and tears followed by severe vomiting and diarrhea. Concomitant symptoms are visual disturbances caused by constriction of the pupil, an irregular, slow pulse rate, decreasing blood pressure, and asthmatic breathing. The patient's mental processes are clear, and he does not experience delirium or hallucinations. In severe cases, death infrequently results from paralysis of the heart or respiratory failure.

A physician should be called immediately. Treatment of muscarine poisoning involves lavage of the patient's stomach, unless this has been rendered unnecessary by the vomiting and diarrhea, and the hypodermic administration of atropine, a specific antidote. After vomiting has ceased, dilute saline solutions and glucose should be administered orally in large amounts.

Ibotenic Acid-Muscimol

The symptoms observed in cases of poisoning resulting from the eating of *Amanita muscaria* (fly agaric) and *A. pantherina* (panther amanita) are due to ibotenic acid and muscimol, two closely related, interconvertible compounds which have similar activities and may therefore be considered an entity. Before these compounds were identified, the designation pilzatropine was applied to the toxic principles in these species since their activity is similar to atropine in certain respects. The term is commonly found in older books on mycology and toxicology.

An additional confusing element is the occurrence of muscarine in both these species and the fact that it has been erroneously designated in the past as the main toxic agent in them. Muscarine does occur in both *Amanita muscaria* and *A. pantherina,* but only in very small amounts, so that the principal effects of poisoning are those of ibotenic acid-muscimol. This is the most common type of mushroom poisoning occurring in the Pacific Northwest, and every collector should learn to recognize the symptoms and be familiar with their treatment.

Symptoms will appear fifteen to thirty minutes after the mushrooms have been eaten. After experiencing a brief period of drowsiness, the patient passes into a state of excitement resembling alcoholic intoxication, characterized by confusion, pronounced muscle spasms, delirium, hallucinations, and disturbances of vision. Following this excited state, which may last for four hours or more, he passes into a deep sleep and later awakes with little or no memory of it. Vomiting occurs only infrequently. Death seldom results and recovery is very rapid, usually within twenty-four hours.

In cases of poisoning of this type, call a physician. The toxic material must be removed from the gastrointestinal tract. Chlorpromazine may be administered to terminate excitement and hallucinations. During the subsequent depression stage, stimulants such as tea or coffee, but not alcohol, may be given. If depression is severe, nikethamide may be employed. Further treatment is largely symptomatic.

It is interesting to note that explorers and travelers who toured Siberia in the early part of the eighteenth century repeatedly confirmed the use of the fly agaric as a narcotic or intoxicant by the Koryak and neighboring tribes of Kamchatka. Vivid descriptions of orgies resulting from the use of this plant are recorded in the literature.

Psilocybin-Psilocin

Accidental ingestion of certain small mushrooms not commonly collected for food purposes can cause the eater to experience hallucinations that are particularly vivid and dramatic. Some species of *Psilocybe* and *Conocybe* have been used as intoxicants for many years by Indians in southern Mexico in their medicoreligious ceremonies. Certain species or strains of *Panaeolus* produce similar effects. Mushrooms of this type that are most likely to be encountered in the Pacific Northwest include *Conocybe cyanopus, Psilocybe baeocystis, P. cyanescens,* and *P. pelliculosa.* Two closely related active principles, psilocybin and psilocin, are present in these mushrooms. The former is usually present in larger quantities, but both have identical physiological actions.

First effects are noted one-half to one hour after eating the mushrooms and continue for several hours. The patient displays anxiety and difficulty in concentration and understanding. Sensitivity to touch, changes in size, shape, color, and depth of vision are also experienced. His mood is altered; usually he feels elated, but he may be depressed. Also very common are elementary hallucinations such as seeing colored lights and patterns when the eyes are closed, and true hallucinations including changes in apparent size, weight, and shape of the body.

If a person displays these symptoms after eating mushrooms, call a physician, and he will administer symptomatic treatment. In serious cases, chlorpromazine or other phenothiazines may be given. Recovery is ordinarily rapid and complete.

GASTROINTESTINAL IRRITANTS

Mushrooms containing compounds that have an irritating actions upon the digestive system include certain acrid species of *Russula (R. emetica), Lactarius (L. torminosus),* and *Boletus (B. eastwoodiae),* as well as *Tricholoma pardinum, Rhodophyllus lividus, Paxillus involutus, Naematoloma fasciculare,* and *Cantharellus floccosus.* Eating them will result in vomiting and mild to extremely severe diarrhea accompanied by abdominal cramps. In most cases, the symptoms terminate spontaneously within a short period of time, and the patient's health is completely restored in a day or two. *Naematoloma fasciculare, Paxillus involutus,* and *Rhodophyllus lividus* are perhaps the most dangerous of all the mushrooms in this category. All three are known to have caused deaths, especially in children or elderly persons.

Call a physician in all cases of poisoning by mushrooms containing gastrointestinal irritants. After removal of the toxic material from the digestive tract, bed rest and proper diet are indicated.

DISULFIRAMLIKE CONSTITUENTS

Disulfiram is a synthetic chemical compound which has

been used for many years by industrial concerns in the vulcanization of rubber. Although it can be taken by man in relatively large doses without any apparent effect, if an alcoholic beverage is consumed after disulfiram has been taken, the patient becomes very ill. Symptoms begin in five to ten minutes. The face feels hot and sweaty and becomes flushed to a purple-red color. This condition spreads rapidly over the neck and chest, breathing becomes rapid and difficult, the heart beats rapidly but blood pressure falls, and the patient experiences a violent headache, dizziness, nausea, vomiting, and great general discomfort. These symptoms last a few hours and are followed by drowsiness and sleep. Disulfiram is used as a drug in the treatment of chronic alcoholics.

Coprinus atramentarius, the inky cap, contains an unidentified active principle which, although not disulfiram, produces the same effects when alcohol is drunk concurrently with or following a meal of the mushrooms. The degree of poisoning will vary from mild to severe according to the amount of mushroom eaten, the quantity of alcohol consumed, and the time interval between the two.

Appearance of the symptoms is often somewhat erratic. In some cases, alcohol may be drunk with impunity immediately after eating the mushroom, but a severe reaction will occur if alcohol is consumed again twenty-four hours later. In other instances, the poisoning may occur immediately after the meal and the alcohol and will recur if more alcohol is consumed even after forty-eight hours. The only safe rule is to refrain from drinking any alcoholic beverage (beer, wine, whisky) for several days both before and after eating *Coprinus atramentarius.* Fortunately, the related species *C. comatus* (shaggy mane), which is noted for its excellent flavor, does not produce this reaction.

If poisoning occurs, call a physician. Recovery is usually spontaneous and complete, but severe cases require symptomatic and supportive treatment.

The Hunt, the Quarry, and the Skillet

By ANGELO M. PELLEGRINI

Having read this book, you are now familiar with the mushroom kingdom. You have learned to distinguish the edible from the poisonous species. Where you are uncertain, you will tread with care. You have gathered some mushrooms; and perhaps you have already designated some species of the edible as your favorites. You are becoming acquainted with the several mushroom areas in your region. And now, thinking of the seasons to come, you visualize yourself returning from those areas with baskets filled with your preferred species.

Along the way, your interest in mushrooms has grown. What was once a curiosity, an interesting phenomenon of nature, you now regard as a food of exquisite taste; and you are beginning to search for ways to enjoy completely the expected harvests. Your problem may be put in these terms: What are some of the ways to manage in the kitchen, for immediate and for later use, the mushrooms gathered in the hills and in the meadows? The answer to this question is the subject of these notes.

Let us proceed with this fiction: You have come to my kitchen with a basket of mushrooms you found in the country. You ask me whether I know the variety, and I immediately recognize it as the meadow mushroom, one of the most savory of all the edible species. You tell me—foolishly, as I shall show later!—precisely where you found them. The time is early June.

You offer to share your treasure with me, and we talk about mushrooms and mushroom cookery. I take from the basket one of the smaller meadow mushrooms, a solid little ball with the cap still tightly closed, clean it with a napkin, and pop it into my mouth. You are surprised, even a little frightened, as if I had done something dangerous. Wild mushrooms are suspect among people who know little about them, and the eating of a raw wild mushroom seems a little foolhardy. However, impressed by the apparent relish with which I am eating the mushroom, you ask whether the meadow mushroom is actually good raw.

I reply that practically all edible mushrooms are good raw, some more so than others. Certain cup fungi and many of the helvellas and their relatives should not be eaten uncooked, and some people have a bad reaction to eating raw morels. What I mean to emphasize is that the *taste* of the raw is generally good and pleasant; and it differs from that of the cooked. This, as you well know, is also true of many vegetables. Thus, in order to taste all the goodness of a mushroom, to explore it fully as a fine food, one ought to eat it raw as well as cooked.

When I ate that mushroom right from your basket, I was being mischievous. One needs some condiment with the raw mushroom, if only a sprinkling of salt. Since you say you are willing to try, I want to make your first experience with raw wild mushrooms as pleasant as I know how. I propose to make for you a raw wild mushroom spread to be eaten on thin slices of good bread. Observe with care; then we shall eat together.

Let us clean six of the smaller mushrooms and peel two shallots. We now mince these together until the shallot-mushroom mixture is about the consistency of ground meat. From my herb garden I take sprigs of parsley and *Mentha pulegium*, commonly known as English pennyroyal. These are minced separately. Half of the mushroom-shallot mixture is put into a small bowl together with a teaspoon of the minced parsley; the other half is put into another bowl with a teaspoon of the minced pennyroyal. Into each bowl we pour a tablespoon of olive oil and a teaspoon of lemon juice. A dash of salt, a sprinkling of pepper, the ingredients thoroughly mixed, and the two are ready. We spread one on two thin slices of bread, lightly toasted, and the other on two other slices. And these we now eat; first the one, then the other.

You search for superlatives to express your gratification. These spreads are delicious; and you are now convinced that raw wild mushrooms, with an appropriate condiment, taste good. Think now of what we have done as but a raw mushroom theme on which we can play several variations. We have herbs in the garden, spices in the kitchen cabinet, wine in the cellar, and mushrooms in the basket. All we need in order to work out some variations is a culinary imagination and a bit of gluttony in our makeup.

You noted, did you not, the striking difference between the spread flavored with parsley and the one flavored with pennyroyal? To vary further the basic recipe we may substitute garlic for shallots, and the other fresh herbs such as tarragon, marjoram, or oregano for the two we have used. Or we may combine several herbs. We may top the spread with paper-thin slices of tomato or avocado. Or why not with a good jack cheese? I have some. Why don't we experiment with the cheese?

We prepare enough of the parsley-flavored spread to cover four slices of bread. We arrange on each a few shreds of the jack cheese and place them under the broiler. While the cheese is melting, I pull the cork from a bottle of Chardonnay; when the broiler has done its work, we eat the spread and sip the wine.

Marvelous! And why not? Quality ingredients were properly put together, and the result is gratifying.

Of course, as you suggest, shallots are expensive, and I happen to have the necessary fresh herbs in my garden. But what about people who have neither? Well, you may substitute green onions or chives for shallots, and dried herbs for fresh ones. But remember that a substitute is no more than a substitute. For example, note how little of the aroma of fresh-picked basil remains in the dried herb from the spice cabinet. These aromatic plants are the very soul of cookery, and you need not be without them. Build yourself a garden and grow your own. It is not beyond your competence, and it is a labor of love. You will find all you need to know, in order thus to enrich yourself, in my book *The Food Lover's Garden*.

And now, back to our theme. Can you suggest further variations? Draw on your kitchen experience; put your culinary imagination to work. We began with a mixture of minced mushrooms, shallots, and an herb. Where can we go from here?

Why not cook the spreads we have made? Any one of them, sautéed in a bit of butter or olive oil—I often prefer a mixture of the two—can be used as a base for a mushroom sauce. For example, I have two lamb chops. We shall make a sauce for them in this way. First, I press a little garlic on the lamb chops, season them with salt and pepper, and put them under the broiler. Now, in a bit of butter and oil, in a small skillet, over low heat, I sauté the mushroom mixture flavored with pennyroyal, using only three of the medium-sized mushrooms. Note that the heat is low and the process unhurried, for we must avoid browning or burning the ingredients. Now I stir in a pinch of flour as a thickening agent; then a quarter of a cup of dry vermouth and a teaspoon of lemon juice, stirring as necessary. When the lemon-vermouth is reduced by half, I add enough stock to produce a fluid but thickish sauce. A slow simmer for a few minutes, and the sauce is done. The lamb chops are now broiled. I take them from the broiler, spread the sauce over them, and put them back under the broiler for about a minute.

We eat them, sizzling hot and nicely aromatized. The Chardonnay was grown especially to accompany these chops. Or so we think; and that's all that matters. You agree that lamb chops thus sophisticated belong in the category of transcendental gastronomy.

Now you are probably wondering how this sauce itself may be varied. That is always the proper, the creative mode in the kitchen. Only on rare occasions must one be slavish to a formula. Variations are seldom created in the abstract. They are normally inspired by necessity, by one's gastronomic mood, the intensity of one's appetite, the materials one has on hand. Hence the importance of a well-stocked pantry and fresh herbs in the garden. How often have I conceived a recipe in the garden while garden labor burned calories and gave edge to the appetite and I surveyed what I had grown on my tiny patch of land! In preparing this mushroom sauce we could achieve something different and equally good by using other herbs, by adding cream, or tomato, or a dash of Tabasco for piquancy. That slight suggestion of peppery fire always adds zest to a morsel and makes it more appetizing.

However, one must always use prudence and restraint in experimenting with such ingredients. Too much fat—butter, oil, cream—recoils on its own too much; it tends to cloy on the educated palate. The flavor of the mushroom must not be overwhelmed, as it often is in restaurants, with too much tomato or too heavy a brown sauce. The spreads we made were nicely balanced. Too much of the herbs or lemon juice would have produced less gratifying results.

We could have used this Chardonnay we are enjoying or any good dry, white wine instead of the vermouth in making the sauce. I often use it, though I prefer the dry vermouth because of the aromatics in its composition.

You ask whether I have a favorite recipe for cooking mushrooms, and how I intend to prepare these meadow mushrooms that you have brought me.

Not in any particularly sophisticated way. After many years of experimentation in the kitchen, I have come to the conclusion that labored refinement and sophistication do not necessarily yield happy results. In order to achieve fine mushroom cookery, little needs to be added to the butter and olive oil but a crush of garlic and a mince of an herb or two.

Tomorrow I shall probably cook the meadow mushrooms in the following way. Slice them. Heat equal parts of olive oil and butter, a generous tablespoon of each for a pound of mushrooms—more if one likes fat and has no fear of it. When it is hot, drop in two cloves of garlic coarsely chopped, a tablespoon of minced parsley, and a teaspoon of minced pennyroyal. When these begin to sizzle in the skillet—and remember not to let them brown or burn!—add the mushrooms, stir briskly, sprinkle with salt and pepper, reduce the heat, and let them cook slowly. That is all.

I have mentioned some of the herbs that may be used. There is another highly recommended by Italian chefs. It is *Nepeta cataria,* catnip or catmint. The Italian name, *nepitella,* is more attractive. Others prefer oregano and call it *erba da funghi,* mushroom grass. The flavor of these herbs harmonizes with that of mushrooms and accentuates it. They both yield excellent results, and either can be used with the indispensable parsley. And mushrooms cooked in this way suggest any number of variations.

To make an excellent mushroom sauce, one may add a liquid—either wine, stock, cream, or tomato. And this reminds me of a dish I must tell you about. Let us simply call it rabbit or fowl, preferably game fowl, to be cooked with mushrooms and eaten with polenta or rice. It is a gluttony burgher's dish, one that generates heat and creates energy—a dish that is therefore appropriate for the fall and winter. In this dish, the wild mushroom is not cooked for its own sake, as a dish in itself; it is used as an auxiliary food, a flavoring ingredient, though easily the star of such ingredients. And, indeed, in all high-level cuisine the mushroom is used more often as a supporting element than as a central one; but the support it gives is actually what gives distinction to the star.

And so it is with—shall we say rabbit stew with mushrooms? I choose rabbit because it is nearer to game than fowl and easier to come by than game. Cut the rabbit into small pieces, dust them lightly with flour, brown them slowly in olive oil and butter, using salt and pepper to taste. Remove them from the skillet; then sauté the mushrooms, a pound or somewhat more for one rabbit, in the fat and meat juice in the way I have already described. Add half a cup of dry white wine and reduce; add a small tin of tomato sauce and an equal measure of stock. Stir well, simmer briefly, correct for seasoning, and finish cooking the rabbit in the sauce. Serve it with rice; or, much better, with polenta.

You may be among those unfortunate ones who do not know what polenta is. It is nothing more than a thick corn-meal mush. To prepare it, drop half a stick of butter into two quarts of boiling, salted water, then stir in enough coarse-ground yellow cornmeal to produce a heavy, thick, grainy paste as solid as bread dough. Add the cornmeal to the boiling water in driblets, stirring constantly with a large wooden spoon until you have achieved the desired density. Cook it over slow heat for about forty-five minutes. When it is done, upend the kettle on a cutting board and let the polenta slip out. Let it rest for a few minutes until it is firm and can be sliced. Arrange a generous slice on a plate and spoon the rabbit or fowl and mushrooms over it. A bit of grated Parmesan cheese scattered on it will add to your delight.

Rabbit and mushroom stew served this way is a great dish. While eating it, one is thankful that he did not die yesterday. And it is the dedicated mushroom hunter's dish, as much as sourdough pancakes are the prospector's dish. Mate it, of course, with the headiest claret or burgundy you can afford.

Any edible variety of mushroom—boletus, chanterelle, shaggy mane, the prince, whatever the hunt yields—can be used in this manner. And, by the way, if you have never eaten fried *Boletus edulis* with fried artichokes, then there is a gastronomic delight for you to anticipate. Frying is one of the best ways to prepare certain mushrooms for the table, especially boletus, morel, shaggy mane, and the meadow mushroom. Cut them into slices about a third of an inch thick, dust them with flour, dip them into beaten egg, and fry them slowly, until nicely browned, in no more olive oil than is necessary to cover well the bottom of the skillet. Pare small artichokes down to the heart, cut them into slices, and treat them the same way. Salt and pepper to taste, and, just before removing them from the pan, squeeze a few drops of lemon juice on them. Prepared in this way, the *Boletus edulis* becomes a culinary classic.

If you are ever so fortunate as to find yourself with a whole shopping bag full of mushrooms, you may want to freeze some of them. Mushrooms can be frozen without any appreciable loss of texture or taste. For best results cook them completely with all seasonings as you would for the table and then freeze them in well-sealed containers. They will keep without noticeable deterioration for more than a year. One may also sauté the mushrooms, seasoned as one likes, and then reduce them to a paste in a blender using, as needed, slight additions of stock to facilitate the transformation. The paste is then frozen in small containers and used when needed to enrich a sauce.

This mushroom paste can be spread on a steak as it broils, or warmed and spread on a slice of roast beef. In either case one must use it rather sparingly for it is concentrated mushroom and too much of it will humble the taste of the beef. When used to season a steak, whether broiled or pan fried, the heated sauce should be spread on the meat after it is done. A minute is all that is required to achieve a proper integration of meat and sauce. A longer time might burn the sauce or dissipate too much of its moisture.

And now let me tell you that if you have never eaten wild mushroom soup, then you have no idea what a delicacy cream of mushroom soup can be. I made it for the first time several years ago out of sheer desperation. I came home from one of the more grim and determined hunts loaded with morels. We could eat only so many. We had already more than we could use in the freezer. What should we do with these? I thought of mushroom soup—which I like very much but had never made. I consulted the cookbooks, only to discover that only one included a recipe for mushroom soup, and that not a very satisfactory one. So I created my own. I cleaned the morels and cooked them partially in butter and oil with shallots and parsley. Then I creamed them in a blender and finished cooking them in chicken broth, just enough of the broth to yield a dense but nicely fluid soup. The only spice I used was a bit of nutmeg. When the soup had simmered for about fifteen minutes I put it into quart jars. The yield was eight quarts. No flour was used, no filler, no thickening agent. The density and substance of the soup were produced by the abundance of morels. And in that state the soup was frozen. A rich cream, about a cup for each quart, would be added later when the soup was thawed and heated for serving. One might also add a bit of dry sherry, but sherry must never be used unless it is dry and of superior quality.

Needless to say, so-called cooking sherry should never be used. Avoid it as you would the plague! Strictly speaking, there is no such thing as cooking sherry or cooking wine. Wine is either ordinary or superior; and only the latter should be used in fine cuisine. Well! We had the last of those eight quarts two years after the soup was made. We thawed it, heated it, added the cream, and served it to guests who were amazed by the age of the soup and its authentic mushroom richness. Later I made mushroom soup using the meadow mushroom, with excellent results. I made it also on another occasion using boletus. The soup was good, but not so good as the morel soup. On another occasion I combined morels and boletus, with gratifying results. In summary, I would be inclined to say that when one comes home from the hunt groaning under a burden of mushrooms, the most advantageous use of the surplus is to convert it into mushroom soup.

Another recommended method of conserving mushrooms is drying them. Any mushroom can be dried; but the one that can be best treated in this way for culinary purposes is the boletus, preferably the *Boletus edulis*. It is this variety that comes to us dry from the Balkans and the Mediterranean and that is so expensive, as much as forty dollars a pound. It is the one mushroom that has a stronger nose when dried than when fresh; and it is the one dried mushroom that great chefs of the Western world prefer above all others in making certain mushroom-flavored sauces. In our home it has always been preferred to the fresh as an ingredient in the classic spaghetti sauce and in making risotto. A scant handful is all one needs to execute the ordinary household recipe.

The procedure for drying mushrooms is not at all complicated. The mushroom is trimmed and cleaned with a soft brush and a paring knife. It is then cut into slices about a quarter of an inch thick, and these are distributed on a screen such as is used in screening soil, or on one made for the purpose by stretching plastic or metal screening over a rectangular frame. The drying should be accomplished in the sun whenever possible, and for this reason one should dry the mushrooms that are hunted in the late spring, when sunny days are more likely to occur than in the fall. Lacking sun, the drying may be done in a warm, well-ventilated room. Before they are stored in tins, jars, or plastic bags, the mushrooms must be tinder-dry. If there is residual moisture, they will generate nasty vermin.

Never wash mushrooms before drying them. Mushrooms are spongy; they absorb water easily, and water thins out their flavor. So, whenever possible, one should cook them without washing them. If they are properly trimmed when they are gathered, especially the root end of the stem, there is very little soil left on them, no more than can be easily removed with a soft brush or moist cloth. When you gathered these meadow mushrooms you failed to trim the stems, so there is considerable dirt strewn among them in the basket, and some of them will have to be washed.

When dried mushrooms are used in cooking—and they are normally used as flavoring agents only—they are first soaked in boiling water, dropped in and stirred for about half a minute in the rolling boil. This frees whatever dirt may be sticking to them. The pan is set aside for a couple of minutes to let dirt particles sink to the bottom; then the mushrooms are lifted with a slotted spoon onto the chopping board. Use no more water than is needed to do the job. When the mushrooms are removed, pour the water carefully off the residue and set it aside. It will be charged with mushroom flavor, and you may want to incorporate some of it into whatever sauce you are making. Remember that this entire process of rendering dried mushrooms soft and pliable requires no more than a couple of minutes. If the mushrooms are left too long in the water, some of the flavor will go down the drain, especially when the water itself is not used.

One more suggestion now regarding the rabbit or fowl dish with mushrooms and polenta. Last spring I came home from a mushroom hunt with ten pounds of prime *Boletus edulis*. After we had eaten our fill, I cooked the surplus in the tomato sauce I described for the rabbit recipe and froze it in a number of small containers. The virtue of this procedure is obvious. When you want the rabbit or fowl with mushrooms, brown the meat, add the packet of frozen mushrooms in tomato sauce, pull the cork from a bottle of whatever red wine you prefer, and call the guests to the dinner table.

My final advice to you is that you learn to be a true mushroom hunter—grim, greedy, and cunning—not a sophisticated dilettante. The mushroom hunter does not gather mushrooms or merely pick them. He hunts them down; and as often as not he finds them when they are not there. Let me explain. What I mean is that the passion, the greed, the grim determination, the cunning, the trained nose—all of these combine to give the mushroom hunter such acuity of perception that he can see a mushroom when it is still under the mulch, invisible to others. When stalking the mushroom, he has no other interests, passions, feelings save an insatiable greed for the quarry. He differs from men who hunt and fish. These may be, and often are, abstemious. When the game is in the bag, their excitement is over. Not so the mushroom hunter.

He drools as he hunts; and as he lunges his way through the tangle of vine maple among conifers in search of *Boletus edulis,* he plots its fate in the skillet. His consuming passion for mushrooms informs his hunt and makes him relentless in it. It accounts for his effectiveness. Thus we cannot separate the hunt from the enjoyment of the quarry; the process is continuous. What was desire in the hills becomes fulfillment in the kitchen. So don't be a mushroom buff, a mere mycologist whose center of interest is the display room or the laboratory. Aspire to be a hunter whose center of interest is his belly.

As such he has a credo and an eccentricity. He hunts only at the crack of dawn and wears his shirt inside out. To ask why is to ask why fire burns. His credo may be stated thus: He has sworn an oath to keep his mushroom patches a secret and to find and poach on the patches of other hunters. When mushrooms are the prize, the scope of all his aspirations is narrowed to these two goals. Though in all else he may be as saintly as Saint Francis, in the pursuit of these ends he is more satanic than Satan. He will betray his nearest and dearest without the slightest twitch of flesh or spirit. He is amoral.

You told me where you found these meadow mushrooms, in the meadow where road *x* crosses road *y*. It was good of you; but it was unpardonable folly. Thanks for your generosity. Now go your way; you are initiated into the tribe of those who have a pagan reverence for mushrooms.

Selected Wild Mushroom Recipes

Compiled by MARGARET McKENNY

A Hunter's Toast

On a tramp through the fields and forests, carry with you a small jar of butter, creamed with salt and pepper. On finding any edible mushroom (except morels or elfin saddles), collect a few dry sticks and fire them. Split a green stick (alder or willow) at one end. Put the mushroom in the cleft, hold it over the fire until tender, season with the butter. Eat from the stick. (*Charles McIlvaine*)

Stuffed Morels

Choose large perfect morels. Dust lightly with flour. Open the stems and cap and stuff with a mixture of chopped cooked chicken livers or chicken and bread crumbs bound with an egg yolk. Season with minced chives and salt and pepper. Butter a casserole, put in stuffed morels, and bake in moderate oven (350° F.) for fifteen minutes. Serve mushrooms in their own gravy, which will be of rich flavor.

Most morels should not be eaten uncooked.

Meadow Mushrooms or Chanterelles with Eggplant

Peel and cut in ¼-inch slices one medium-sized eggplant. Sauté in 2 tablespoons of oil until tender. Drain off surplus fat. Chop 1 cup of mushrooms into small pieces and dredge lightly with flour. Chop 1 small onion and 1 green pepper and sauté in butter. Add 1½ cups cooked tomatoes, seasoned with salt, pepper, chili powder, and a pinch of basil. Place the eggplant slices in a casserole and pour over them the

225

mushrooms combined with the tomato sauce. Garnish with seasoned and buttered crumbs, bake in medium oven twenty minutes.

Chanterelles with Ham

Sauté 1 cup of chopped chanterelles, lightly dredged with flour, with 1 small minced onion. Add ½ cup minced ham and 2 tablespoons of sour cream. Cook without boiling until the mixture thickens, season with pepper and minced parsley. Serve on rounds of toast.

Baked Sparassis

Pull into pieces, clean, and dredge lightly with flour. Add 2 tablespoons butter, melted, with 1 teaspoon of minced onion, a little salt, and freshly ground white pepper. Sauté gently until tender. Put in casserole with seasoned crumbs on top and bake.

Mushroom Canapés

Sauté 1 cup of calves' or chicken liver with 1 small minced onion until brown, then add 1 cup of finely ground lean ham. Sauté 1 cup chopped meadow mushrooms or chanterelles and add to liver and ham mixture. If the mixture is too thin, thicken with 1 teaspoon of flour rubbed with 1 teaspoon of butter. Season to taste with freshly ground pepper and a dash of cayenne pepper. The mixture should be thick enough to spread on rounds of buttered toast. Finish by sifting finely crumbled yolks of hard-boiled eggs over the surface. (*Marilyn Harlin*)

Hungarian-Style Mushrooms

Sauté 1 cup chopped meadow mushrooms, *ceps,* chanterelles, or blewits in 1 tablespoon of butter seasoned with salt, pepper, and paprika; then add ½ cup sour cream and simmer, not boil, for five minutes. Serve immediately on toast.

Greek-Style Mushrooms

Marinate overnight 1 cup of chopped chanterelles in 2 tablespoons of olive oil and 2 tablespoons of white wine vinegar seasoned with salt, pepper, minced onion or garlic, and minced parsley. Cook in mixture. Let cool. Serve as hors d'oeuvres, adding lemon juice before serving. If the mixture stands for a day in the refrigerator it is all the better.

Marinated Wild Mushrooms

Combine ¼ cup olive oil, 2 tablespoons lemon juice or vinegar, ¼ teaspoon ginger, salt, and freshly ground pepper to taste. Add a crushed clove of garlic to this marinade and let it stand for 1 hour. Remove the garlic and marinate in the dressing 1 pound button meadow mushrooms, small chanterelles, or tender pieces of sulphur polypore. Drain the mushrooms and serve them on cocktail picks.

Weaned Russula

As this large mushroom is rather coarse it is better to chop it into fine pieces before sautéing. It may also be chopped, combined with cracker crumbs and beaten egg, adding freshly ground pepper and a little salt, made into patties, dipped in beaten egg, and fried in deep fat.

Sukiyaki

Slice 1 cup of Japanese armillaria *(matsutake)*. Cut up 1 cup celery, 1 cup green pepper, and 1 cup fat green onions into 1-inch pieces.

Have the butcher cut ¼ pound of tender beef into very thin strips. Put the mushrooms and beef in the center of a large frying pan, put the celery in one corner, pepper in another, and onions in another. Then pour in 1 cup of soy sauce and ½ cup of saki or a dry white wine, and stew the combined ingredients (covered) until the beef and mushrooms are tender. The vegetables will be cooked, but still crisp.

Have ready a bowl of cooked rice, dry and fluffy, put a generous helping on a plate, place beef, mushrooms and vegetables—a tablespoonful of each—on the rice, and spoon the sauce over all. Serves four.

This recipe may be varied by using cooked chicken or pork sliced very thin. Other mushrooms can be substituted for the Japanese, but they should be firm, like chanterelles or the sulphur polypore.

Creamed Wild Mushrooms with Chicken Livers

Sauté 1 pound chicken livers in ¼ cup butter until brown. Add 1 cup thinly sliced boletus, meadow mushrooms, chanterelles, or oyster mushrooms and simmer all together for 10 minutes. Stir in 1 cup cream and 2 tablespoons sauterne, heat the cream, and serve the mushrooms and chicken livers at once. *(Faith Watson)*

Deviled Wild Mushrooms

Chop finely 1 pound meadow mushrooms or chanterelles. Sprinkle the mushrooms and 1 small onion, finely chopped, with flour and sauté them in 2 tablespoons butter until they are delicately browned. Add 1 cup chicken bouillon, ½ teaspoon chili powder, 1 teaspoon Worcestershire sauce, a clove of garlic, crushed, and salt to taste. Cook the mixture, stirring, until it is as thick as heavy cream. Discard the garlic clove and cool the sauce. Stir in 3 egg yolks lightly beaten. Divide mushrooms and sauce among small individual ramekins, sprinkle with bread crumbs, dot with butter, and sprinkle with grated Parmesan cheese. Bake the ramekins in a moderate oven (350° F.) for 15 minutes.

Wild Mushrooms with Spanish Sauce

Sauté in 2 tablespoons butter 2 onions, 1 green pepper, and 1 clove of garlic, all chopped, until the vegetables are tender. Add 1 pound chopped button meadow mushrooms or small chanterelles and cook for 2 minutes longer. Add 2 cups tomato purée and 1 teaspoon each of chili powder and salt. Simmer the sauce gently for 1 hour. Serve with chicken.

Wild Mushroom Soup

Chop coarsely 1 pound meadow mushrooms or chanterelles. Roll the pieces in flour and sauté them gently in 2 tablespoons butter until they are tender. Do not allow them to brown. Add 2 cups milk and 1 cup cream. Season the soup with salt and pepper, a dash of onion juice, and 1 teaspoon minced parsley, and serve hot.

Creamed Chicken-of-the-Woods

Cut up 1 pound of the tender edges of sulphur polypore or chicken-of-the-woods caps. Sauté the pieces very slowly in 2 tablespoons butter until they have absorbed most of the butter. Sprinkle them with 1 tablespoon flour and add 1 cup cream. Simmer the sauce until it thickens slightly. Season the mushrooms with salt and freshly ground black pepper and serve them on rounds of freshly made toast.

Chanterelle Fritters

Wash, dry, and chop coarsely small chanterelles. Sauté the pieces in 2 tablespoons butter for 10 minutes. Season the mushrooms with salt and pepper and drain any excess butter from the pan. Sift ½ cup flour and a pinch of salt into a bowl and stir in 1 egg, beaten, and 1 tablespoon melted butter. Add gradually ½ cup flat beer, stirring only until the mixture is smooth, and let the batter rest for 1 hour in a warm place. Fold in 1 egg white, beaten stiff, and the sautéed mushrooms. Drop the batter by spoonfuls into deep hot fat (370° F.) and fry the fritters until they are golden brown. Drain on absorbent paper and sprinkle with salt. Serve immediately.

Chanterelle Soufflé

Wash 2 cups chanterelles and snip 1 fine specimen around the top so that it may be opened out for garnish. Cut the remainder into small pieces. Peel and chop 3 shallots, mash 2 small cloves of garlic (optional). Brown the shallots and garlic in 2 tablespoons of butter in large, deep skillet or saucepan. Add the chanterelles and sauté until golden.

Remove chanterelles from pan, setting aside the one for garnish. Add 3 tablespoons flour to pan, and stir until flour browns lightly. Add 2 tablespoons butter and stir until smooth paste is formed. Add ½ cup hot concentrated consommé and ½ cup milk or light cream. Cook, stirring with whisk or slotted spoon, until very thick and smooth. Add ¼ cup of sherry, ¼ cup of sour cream, and stir over very low heat until it all fuses into a smooth blend (do not boil). Season with salt, pepper, a dash of cayenne, a little grated nutmeg, and 2 tablespoons of Parmesan cheese. Add the finely cut chanterelles, remove from heat to cool.

Beat 4 egg yolks slightly, add to mushrooms in cooled sauce. Beat 5 egg whites until stiff but not dry, and fold ½ of the egg whites thoroughly into the mixture, then add the remaining egg whites, folding them in very lightly.

Butter a 1½-quart soufflé dish and tie a collar of waxed paper around it. Fill with the soufflé mixture and bake in a hot oven (425° F.) for 30 minutes. Open the oven door gently, place chanterelle garnish over the top, close the door again, and bake for about 5 minutes. While the diners wait with warm plates, remove soufflé from oven, remove collar and serve at once. (*Sylvia Schur, Creative Food Consultant*)

Tournedos Woodland

Sauté lightly ½ pound of chanterelles or other wild mushroom with one bunch of minced shallots or young onions. Set aside. Sauté eight *tournedos* (thin slices of *filet mignon*), add salt and freshly ground pepper, and flambé with 2 tablespoons of brandy. Combine with mushrooms and shallots and add 1 cup of sauce bordelaise or basic brown sauce, seasoning with one teaspoon of *fines herbes.* Pour over *tournedos* and heat without boiling, adding a pinch of wild thyme just before serving. Sufficient for four. (*Albert Stockli, Four Seasons Restaurant*)

Veal Medaillons Sauté Gourmet

Sauté thoroughly in oil or butter four *medaillons* (thin slices of veal which have been flattened by the butcher). Set aside where they will keep warm, first seasoning with salt and freshly ground pepper.

In the pan where the veal was cooked, pour one cup of white wine. Simmer until reduced one-half, then add one cup of heavy cream. Sauté without discoloring ½ pound of chanterelles mixed with six minced shallots or young onions. Add to sauce. If too thin, thicken with ½ tablespoon of flour rubbed with one tablespoon of butter, bring to a boil, pour over the veal and serve. (*Albert Stockli, Four Seasons Restaurant*)

Spiced Mushroom Relish for Meat

1½ *pounds small whole button mushrooms (meadow mushrooms or honey mushrooms)*
2 *tbsp. butter or oil*
1 *tbsp. flour*
⅛ *tbsp. ground nutmeg*
⅛ *tbsp. ground ginger*
1 *tbsp. brown sugar*
½ *cup dry sherry*

Melt butter in a heavy skillet over a slow fire and blend in the flour, spices, and sugar. Add the mushrooms and stir carefully for 15 minutes. Stir the sherry in gently and serve immediately. Best with baked ham. (*Oregon Mycological Society*)

Scalloped Mushrooms with Oysters

¼ cup mushrooms (chanterelles or red-juice milky cap)
1 pint Pacific oysters, cut in pieces
3 tbsp. butter
½ cup chopped parsley
4 young green onions, chopped tops and all
6 to 8 ounces of sour cream
1 cup fine dry bread crumbs

Use a heavy frying pan. Slice the mushrooms through cap and stem. Stir in the melted butter for 5 minutes. Put all the other ingredients except the oysters into the skillet and combine. Butter the casserole, put in a layer of mix, top with half of the oysters, some sour cream, sprinkle with nutmeg, salt, and pepper, and repeat. Top with layer of mix and a little sour cream. Bake at 350° F. for 25 to 30 minutes. (*Oregon Mycological Society*)

Tamale Loaf with Mushrooms

1½ pounds beef, chuck or round
½ tsp. paprika
2 cups beef stock
3 teaspoons salt
2 cups strained, cooked tomatoes
1½ cups sliced raw mushrooms (meadow mushrooms or boletus)
1 large onion, chopped fine
1 tsp. chili powder
1¼ cups cornmeal

Cover the meat with water and simmer until tender, adding water if necessary. Put the meat through a grinder, and add the two cups of stock. Add the next five ingredients, bring slowly to a boil, and add the cornmeal gradually, stirring constantly. Cook for one hour in a double boiler. Pour into greased molds. Unmold when cold; reheat in a steamer or in the oven and serve with highly seasoned tomato sauce to which more mushrooms and chili powder have been added. (*Oregon Mycological Society*)

Hydnum or Hedgehog Mushrooms

The spreading hydnum can be cooked in any way you would cook chanterelles. It is tender and of good flavor and appreciated because it comes so late in the fall.

Spreading Hydnum Oriental

Combine in a large bowl:
- 1/4 *medium head of cauliflower, sliced thin*
- 1 *zucchini, sliced*
- 6 *chopped green onions, including tops*
- 4 *stalks celery, sliced in 1/4 inch pieces*
- 2 *carrots, sliced thin*
- 1 *green pepper, sliced*
- 1/2 *pound spreading hydnum, sliced*

In a heavy skillet melt half a stick of butter or margarine. Add vegetables, including mushrooms, all at once and sauté for five minutes, tossing gently. Add 1 teaspoon of beef concentrate, 2 tablespoons of water and cover. Simmer for one minute. *(Oregon Mycological Society)*

Woodland Salad

Marinate thinly sliced button meadow mushrooms, small chanterelles, or woodland russulas in French dressing for 1 hour. Add them to a tossed salad of endive and water cress, or any greens you prefer.

Puffballs

Be sure puffballs of any size or species are white all through. As they mature they grow yellow and become bitter. If small, cut through the center to be sure you do not have a white amanita. The puffball is all white flesh, while the amanita shows the outline of cap and stem.

To cook the giant puffball remove the skin if it is tough,

cut into slices ¼ inch thick, dredge lightly with flour, and sauté in butter. Season with salt and pepper after cooking so as to preserve the delicate flavor.

The slices of puffball may be baked in a casserole with alternate layers of buttered bread crumbs, the whole covered with eggs beaten up in milk seasoned with pepper and salt, and topped with buttered, seasoned crumbs, over which has been sifted a little grated Parmesan cheese.

Coral Mushroom

Cut in half, sauté in butter or oil, then stew in double boiler, covered with a little water. When tender, add milk or cream thickened with butter rubbed in flour. Add pepper and salt last as salt toughens the plant.

If, on cutting, center is gelatinous, discard the mushroom.

Bibliography

Atkinson, G. F. *Mushrooms, Edible, Poisonous, etc.* New York: Hafner Publishing Co., reprint 1961.

Bandoni, R. J., and A. F. Szczawinski. *Guide to Common Mushrooms of British Columbia.* British Columbia Provincial Museum Handbook No. 24. Victoria, B.C.: A. Sutton, 1964.

Brightman, F. H., and B. E. Nicholson. *The Oxford Book of Flowerless Plants.* Oxford: Oxford University Press, 1966.

Frieden, L. von *Mushrooms of the World.* New York: Bobbs-Merrill, 1969.

Groves, J. W. *Edible and Poisonous Mushrooms of Canada.* Ottowa, Ont.: Canada Department of Agriculture, 1962.

Hesler, L. R. *Mushrooms of the Great Smokies.* Knoxville: University of Tennessee Press, 1960.

Kauffman, C. H. *The Agaricaceae of Michigan.* New York: Johnson Reprint Corp., reprint 1965.

Krieger, L. C. C. *The Mushroom Handbook.* New York: Dover Publications, reprint 1967.

Kleijn, H. *Mushrooms and Other Fungi.* Garden City, N.Y.: Doubleday and Co., 1962.

Lange, M., and F. B. Hora. *A Guide to Mushrooms and Toadstools.* New York: E. P. Dutton and Co., 1967.

McIlvaine, C., and R. K. Macadam. *One Thousand American Fungi.* Indianapolis, Ind.: Bobbs-Merrill, 1912.

McKenny, M. *Mushrooms of Field and Wood.* New York: John Day Co., 1929.

Pilát, A., and O. Ušák. *Mushrooms.* Amsterdam: H. W. Bijl, 1954.

Ramsbottom, J. *Mushrooms and Toadstools.* London: Collins, 1953.

Rolfe, R. F., and F. W. Rolfe. *The Romance of the Fungus World.* London: Chapman and Hall, 1925.

Seaver, F. J. *The North American Cup-Fungi (Operculates).* New York: Hafner Publishing Co., reprint 1961.

Smith, A. H. *Mushrooms in Their Natural Habitats.* Portland, Ore.: Sawyer's, 1949.

Smith, A. H. *The Mushroom Hunter's Field Guide.* Revised and Enlarged. Ann Arbor: University of Michigan Press, 1964.

Smith, A. H., and H. D. Thiers. *The Boletes of Michigan.* Ann Arbor: University of Michigan Press, 1971.

Thomas, W. S. *Field Book of Common Mushrooms.* New York: G. P. Putnam's Sons, 1948.

Index

Roman numerals refer to color plates.

King Boletus *Boletus edulis* (p. 3)

Yellow-fleshed Boletus *Boletus chrysenteron* (p. 8)

PLATE I

Slippery Jack   *Boletus luteus* (p. 14)

Slippery Jack   *Boletus granulatus* (p. 15)

PLATE II

Woolly-capped Boletus   *Boletus tomentosus* (p. 17)

Yellow Chanterelle   *Cantharellus cibarius* (p. 20)

PLATE III

Pig's Ears   *Cantharellus clavatus* (p. 23)

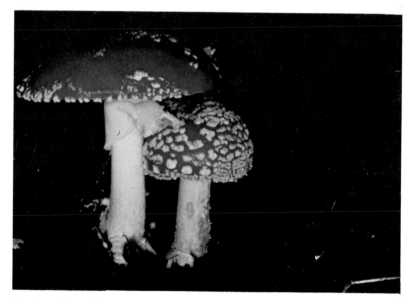

Fly Amanita   *Amanita muscaria* (p. 29)

PLATE IV

Panther Amanita   *Amanita pantherina* (p. 31)

Warted Amanita   *Amanita aspera* (p. 34)

PLATE V

Shaggy Lepiota   *Lepiota rachodes* (p. 43)

Japanese Armillaria or Matsutake   *Armillaria ponderosa* (p. 43)

PLATE VI

Zeller's Armillaria   *Armillaria zelleri* (p. 45)

Red-Brown Tricholoma   *Tricholoma pessundatum* (p. 51)

PLATE VII

Streaked Tricholoma *Tricholoma portentosum* (p. 54)

Red-tufted Wood Tricholoma *Tricholomopsis rutilans* (p. 56)

PLATE VIII

Sweat-producing Clitocybe   *Clitocybe dealbata (sudorifica)* (p. 58)

Smoky-Brown Clitocybe   *Clitocybe avellaneialba* (p. 62)

PLATE IX

Bitter False Paxillus   *Leucopaxillus amarus* (p. 67)

Cone-shaped Waxy Cap   *Hygrophorus conicus* (p. 69)

PLATE X

Scarlet Waxy Cap   *Hygrophorus miniatus* (p. 71)

Sooty-Brown Waxy Cap   *Hygrophorus camarophyllus* (p. 76)

PLATE XI

Woodland Russula   *Russula xerampelina* (p. 84)

Rose-Red Russula   *Russula rosacea* (p. 88)

PLATE XII

Delicious Milky Cap   *Lactarius deliciosus* (p. 94)

Red-Juice Milky Cap   *Lactarius sanguifluus* (p. 95)

PLATE XIII

Slimy Milky Cap *Lactarius mucidus* (p. 98)

Pitted Milky Cap *Lactarius scrobiculatus* (p. 99)

PLATE XIV

Red Milky Cap *Lactarius rufus* (p. 101)

Common Laccaria *Laccaria laccata* (p. 103)

PLATE XV

Purple Laccaria   *Laccaria amethystina* (p. 103)

Clustered Collybia   *Collybia acervata* (p. 105)

PLATE XVI

Velvet-Stem Flammulina   *Flammulina (Collybia) velutipes* (p. 107)

Fairy Ring Mushroom   *Marasmius oreades* (p. 109)

PLATE XVII

Woods Blewits   *Lepista nuda* (p. 112)

Golden Pholiota   *Phaeolepiota aurea* (p. 117)

PLATE XVIII

Gypsy Mushroom   *Rozites (Pholiota) caperata* (p. 118)

Violet Cortinarius   *Cortinarius violaceus* (p. 123)

PLATE XIX

Purple-staining Cortinarius   *Cortinarius mutabilis* (p. 126)

Common Paxillus   *Paxillus involutus* (p. 128)

PLATE XX

Turnip-Bulb Inocybe *Inocybe napipes* (p. 131)

Autumnal Galerina *Galerina autumnalis* (p. 134)

PLATE XXI

Meadow Mushroom *Agaricus campestris* (p. 136)

The Prince *Agaricus augustus* (p. 137)

PLATE XXII

Flat-Top Mushroom   *Agaricus placomyces* (or *meleagris?*) (p. 138)

Woolly-stemmed Agaricus   *Agaricus subrutilescens* (p. 143)

PLATE XXIII

Questionable Stropharia   *Stropharia ambigua* (p. 146)

Smoky-gilled Woodlover   *Naematoloma capnoides* (p. 150)

PLATE XXIV

Rosy Gomphidius   *Gomphidius subroseus* (p. 151)

Colorful Gomphidius   *Chroogomphus (Gomphidius) rutilus* (p. 153)

PLATE XXV

Shaggy Mane   *Coprinus comatus* (p. 154)

Inky Cap   *Coprinus atramentarius* (p. 156)

PLATE XXVI

Thick-skinned Puffballs *Scleroderma* (p. 167)

Chicken-of-the-Woods *Polyporus sulphureus* (p. 169)

PLATE XXVII

Spreading-Hedgehog Mushroom *Dentinum (Hydnum) repandum* (p. 173)

Purple-tipped Coral *Ramaria (Clavaria) botrytis* (p. 182)

PLATE XXVIII

Yellow Coral   *Ramaria flava* (p. 182)

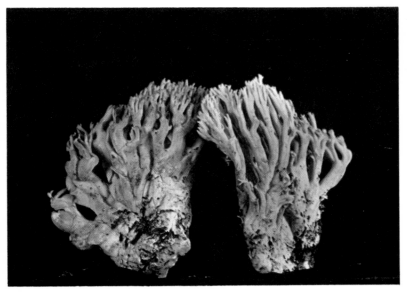

Gelatinous Coral   *Ramaria gelatinosa* (p. 185)

PLATE XXIX

Rose Coral *Ramaria subbotrytis* (p. 187)

Witch's Butter *Dacrymyces palmatus* (p. 188)

PLATE XXX

White Jelly Mushroom　*Pseudohydnum gelatinosum* (p. 189)

Apricot Jelly Mushroom　*Phlogiotis helvelloides* (p. 191)

PLATE XXXI

Orange Fairy Cup *Aleuria aurantia* (p. 192)

Giant Helvella *Gyromitra gigas* (p. 198)

PLATE XXXII